LATIN AMERICAN
All
Organ

Arranged by Bill Woodward

WISE PUBLICATIONS
LONDON/NEW YORK

DISTRIBUTION
MUSIC SALES LIMITED
78 NEWMAN STREET
LONDON WIP 3LA

DESIGN
GEORGE HARDIE
NTA STUDIOS

Granada

English Words by
DOROTHY DODD

Music by
AGUSTÍN LARA

SUGGESTED REGISTRATIONS

Single-Manual Organs
8' 4' I II III V

Vibrato: On
Play: Upper & Lower

General Electronic & Pipe Organs
Upper: Flute 8' 4' 2' Mixture 2' Strings 8'
Lower: Flute 8' 4' Diapason 8'
Pedal: 16 + 8
Vibrato: On

Drawbar Organs
Upper: 80 7634 555
Lower: (00) 6543 221 (0)
Pedal: 4 - (2)
Vibrato: On

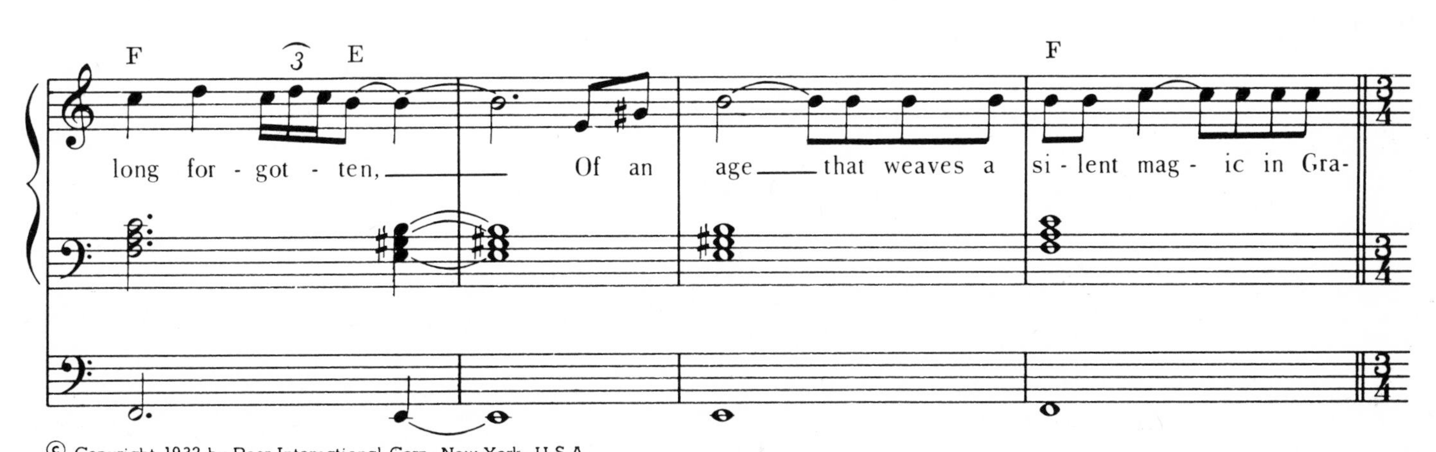

a tempo
F
E
F
-na - da to - day.
E
Mosso
C
C6
Cmaj7
The dawn in the sky greets the day with a
when day is done and the sun starts to
Ebo
ten.
G7
3
sigh for Gra - na - da.
set in Gra - na - da.
ten.
For she can re - mem - ber the splen - dour that once was Gra -
I en - vy the blush of the snow - clad Si - er - ra Ne -

to Coda
C
na - da
na - da
It still can be
found in the hills all a - round as I wan - der a - long
C6
Cmaj7
C6
Em
B7
Em
En - tranc'd by the beau - ty be fore me, En-
tranc'd by a land full of sun - shine and flow - ers and song. And
B7
Em
G7
D.S. al Coda

CODA
C
C7
F
For soon it will wel-come the stars while a
Fm
C
Fm6
C
Broadly
thous-and gui-tars play a soft hab-an-er-a Then
Fm
C
Ebo
G7
moon-lit Gra-na-da will live a-gain the glo-ry of yes-ter-day ro-
Fm6
C
Fm6
C
G7
C
-man-tic and gay.

Pablo The Dreamer

ADIOS MUCHACHOS

English Lyric by
ROBERTO LOPEZ

Music by
JULIO SANDERS

SUGGESTED REGISTRATIONS

Single-Manual Organs
8' I II III
Vibrato: On
Play: Upper & Lower

General Electronic & Pipe Organs
Upper: Cello 8' (or Trumpet 8')
Lower: Flute 8' 4' (or Melodia 8')
Pedal: 16 + 8
Vibrato: On

Drawbar Organs
Upper: 00 4545 440
Lower: (00) 5403 000 (0)
Pedal: 3 - (2)
Vibrato: On

C E7 F F G7 F G7
Pab - lo he's con - tent to be a dream - er, 'neath his som - brer - o he lets all
F C C7 F Fm
care go; For since one ma - gic night be - side the Ri - o Grand - e, His heart was
C D9 G7 C E7
stol - en and he's so in love, He's dream - ing of a mai - den, her lips were hon - ey
Am Ebo G7 C C7
la - den, her eyes were like the moon-glow be - fore the ro - sy dawn, She whis-pered "Won't you

F Fm C E♭o Dm7 D9 G7
kiss me, I hope you'll miss me, We'll meet a - gain, A - mi - go" and she was
C C E7 F
gone. They call him Pab - lo and they laugh while he is dream - ing, Some think he's
F G7 F G7 F C C7
laz - y, Some think he cra - zy; He does - n't care, why should he share the thrill that
F Fm6 C D9 G7
fills him, Be - cause some - day his dreams will all come true.

Besame Mucho

(KISS ME MUCH)

English Words by
SUNNY SKYLAR

Music by
CONSUELO VELAZQUEZ

SUGGESTED REGISTRATIONS

Single-Manual Organs
8' 2' I II III V
Vibrato: On
Play: Upper & Lower

General Electronic & Pipe Organs
Upper: Strings 8'
Lower: Flute 8' 4' (or Melodia 8')
Pedal: 8'
Vibrato: On

Drawbar Organs
Upper: 00 4544 222
Lower: (00) 7756 310 (0)
Pedal: 3 - (2)
Vibrato: On

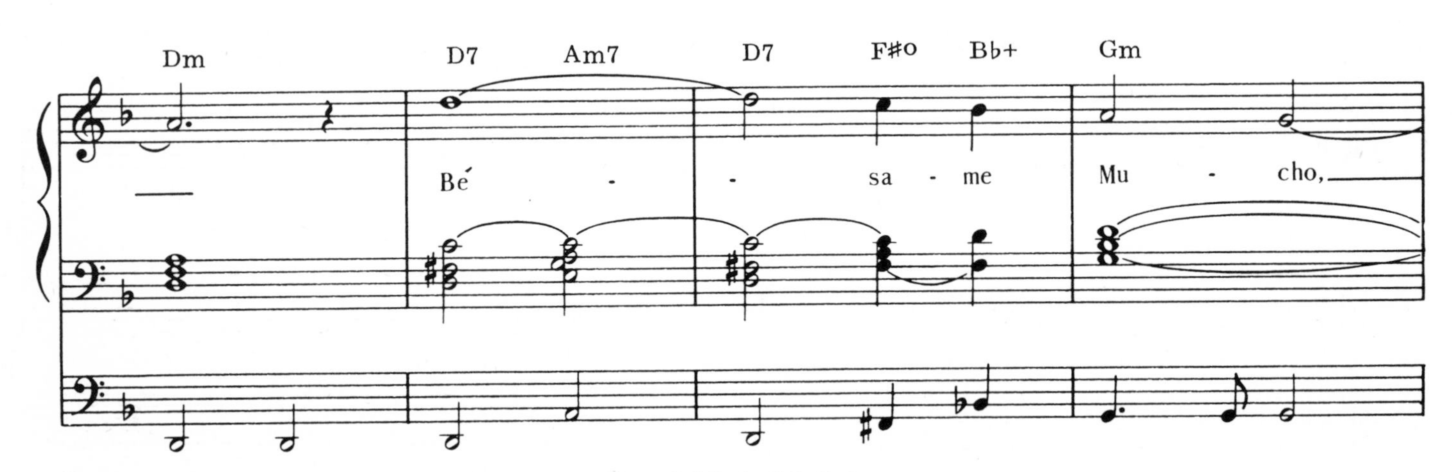

Dm
E7b9
A7
Hold me, my dar - ling and say that you'll al - ways be
Dm Gm7 Dm
Gm
Dm
mine.
This joy is some-thing new, My arms en - fold - ing you
A7 Gm6
Dm
Gm
Nev-er knew this thrill be - fore;
Who - ev - er thought I'd be -
Dm
E7
Bb7
A7
hold - ing you close to me,
Whisp 'ring "It's you I a - dore."

Dm
Gm6
Dm
3
Gm
Dear - est one,
if you should leave me,
Gm
3
F#o
3
Gm
3
A7
3
Dm
A7
Each lit - tle dream would take
wing and my life would be
through;
Dm
D7
Am7
D7
F#o Bb+
Gm
Bé - - sa - me
Mu - cho;
Dm
3
3
E9b
3
A7
3
A7+
Dm
Gm6
Dm
Love me for - ev - er and
make all my dreams come
true.

You Belong To My Heart

(SOLAMENTE UNA VEZ)

English Words by
RAY GILBERT

Music by
AGUSTÍN LARA

SUGGESTED REGISTRATIONS

Single-Manual Organs		General Electronic & Pipe Organs		Drawbar Organs	
8' 4' 2' I II		Upper:	Flute 16' 8' 4' 2' Trumpet 8'	Upper:	86 8757 234
Vibrato:	On	Lower:	Flute 8' 4' Diapason 8'	Lower:	(00) 8763 321 (0)
Play:	Upper & Lower	Pedal:	16 + 8	Pedal:	6 – (4)
		Vibrato:	On	Vibrato:	On

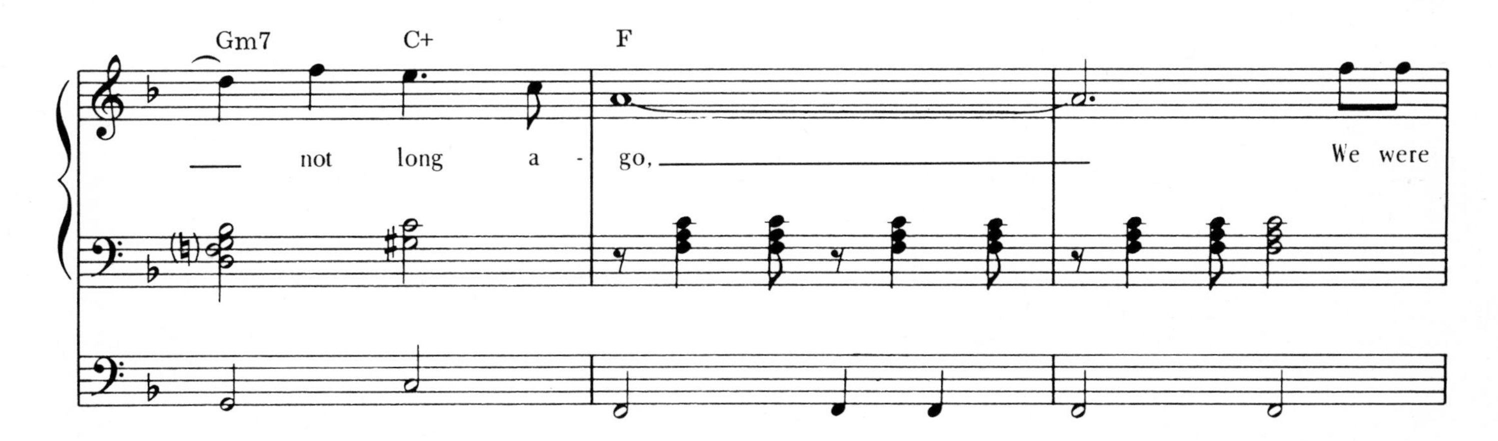

Am
F6
F
D
F#o
C7
gath - er - ing stars while a
mil - lion gui - tars played our
love; song;
When I
said "I love you," ev - 'ry
beat of my heart said it
F
F+7
Dm
C7
F
C6
too.
'Twas a mo - ment like
this,
F6
F#o
C7
do you re -
mem - ber?
And your eyes threw a

Gm D+ Gm7 C+ F
kiss when they met mine;
Am F6 F D F#o
Now we own all the stars and a mil - lion gui - tars are still
C7
play - thing; Dar - ling, you are the song and you'll
C6 C7 Gm7 C7 F Am Abm6 F6
al - ways be - long to my heart.

Love Me With All Of Your Heart

(CUANDO CALIENTA EL SOL)

English Lyric by
MICHAEL VAUGHN

Music by
CARLOS RIGUAL &
CARLOS A. MARTINOLI

SUGGESTED REGISTRATIONS

Single-Manual Organs
8' II IV
Vibrato: On
Play: Upper & Lower

General Electronic & Pipe Organs
Upper: Flute 8' 4' Quint, Nazard
Lower: Flute 8' 4' Diapason 8'
Pedal: 8
Vibrato: On

Drawbar Organs
Upper: 40 7634 555
Lower: (00) 5641 100 (0)
Pedal: 4 - (2)
Vibrato: On

Em
F
G7
C
Am
win - ter ev - 'ry sum - mer ev - 'ry fall.
When we are far a - part or when you're
Em
F6
G9
C6
A7
near me,
Love me with all of your heart as I love you;
Dm
G7
C
Am
Don't give me your love for a mo - ment or an hour,
Love me
Em
F
G7
C6
al - ways as you lov'd me from the start, With ev - 'ry beat of your heart.

History Of Love

(HISTORIA DE UN AMOR)

English Lyric by
DOROTHY DODD

Music by
CARLOS ALMARAN

SUGGESTED REGISTRATIONS

Single-Manual Organs
8' I II III
Vibrato: On
Play: Upper & Lower

General Electronic & Pipe Organs
Upper: Cello 8' (or Trumpet 8')
Lower: Flute 8' 4' (or Melodia 8')
Pedal: 16 + 8
Vibrato: On

Drawbar Organs
Upper: 00 4545 440
Lower: (00) 5403 000 (0)
Pedal: 3 - (2)
Vibrato: On

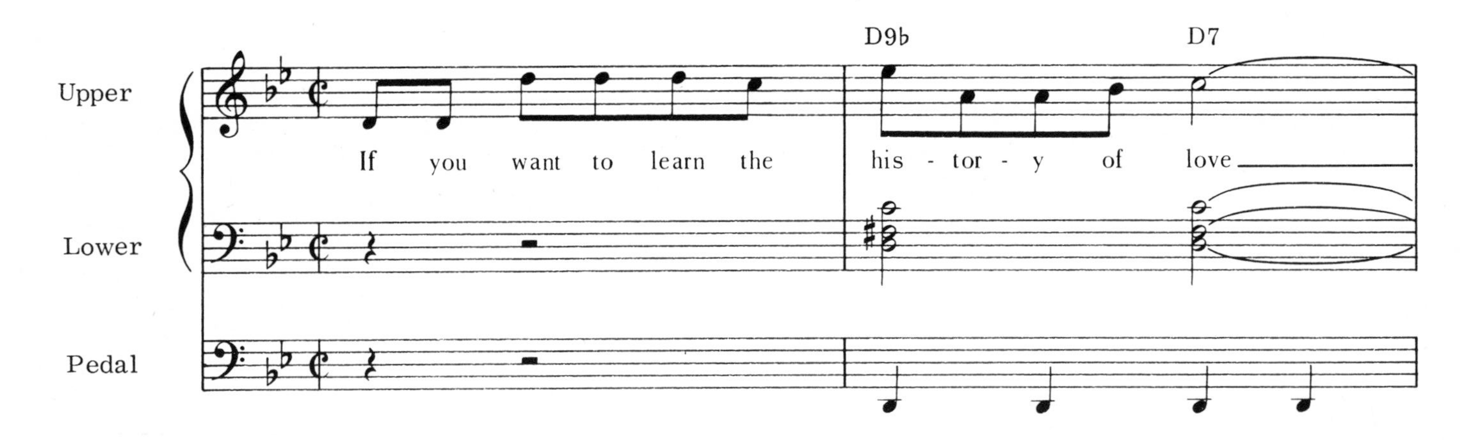

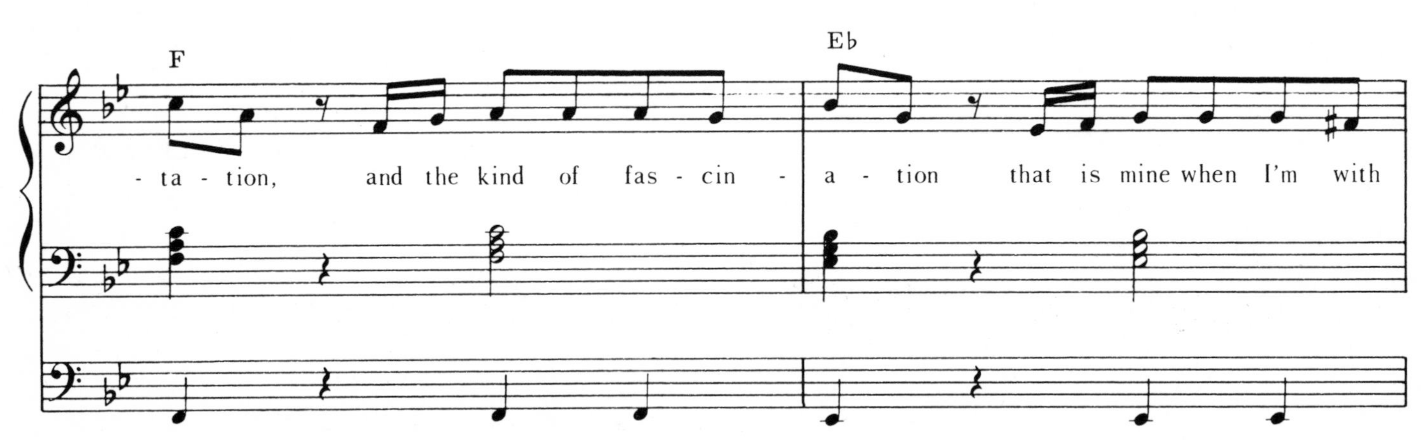

D
you.
Love's a sto - ry that be -
D9♭
gins but nev - er
D7
ends.
And if on - ly we were
Gm
slight - ly clos - er friends,
We could stu - dy it to -
F
geth - er, And per - haps dis - cov - er
E♭
wheth - er,
Cm6
all it says
D7
is real - ly
Gm
true!
Love's a feell ing that we

Cm6
D7
don't ev - er quite un - der - stand 'Till we hear a cer - tain
Gm
Cm Cm7
voice, feel the touch of a hand Then the ma - gic of the ag - es,
F7
Bb Bbmaj7 Bb6
will be there for us to see; Ev-'ry time we turn the
Cm
Am7b5
D7
pag - es, meant for on - ly you and me.

D9♭
D7
If you won - der why I'm tell - ing you to - night
It's be - cause your lips have giv - en me the right,
Gm
Soft - ly yield - ing their per - mis - sion to pre-pare our own e - di - tion of the his - tor - y of love.
F
E♭
Cm6
D7
Gm

Without You

(TRES PALABRAS)

English Lyric by
RAY GILBERT

Music by
OSVALDO FARRES

SUGGESTED REGISTRATIONS

Single-Manual Organs
8' 2' I II III V
Vibrato: On
Play: Upper & Lower

General Electronic & Pipe Organs
Upper: Strings 8'
Lower: Flute 8' 4' (or Melodia 8')
Pedal: 8'
Vibrato: On

Drawbar Organs
Upper: 00 4544 222
Lower: (00) 7756 310 (0)
Pedal: 3 - (2)
Vibrato: On

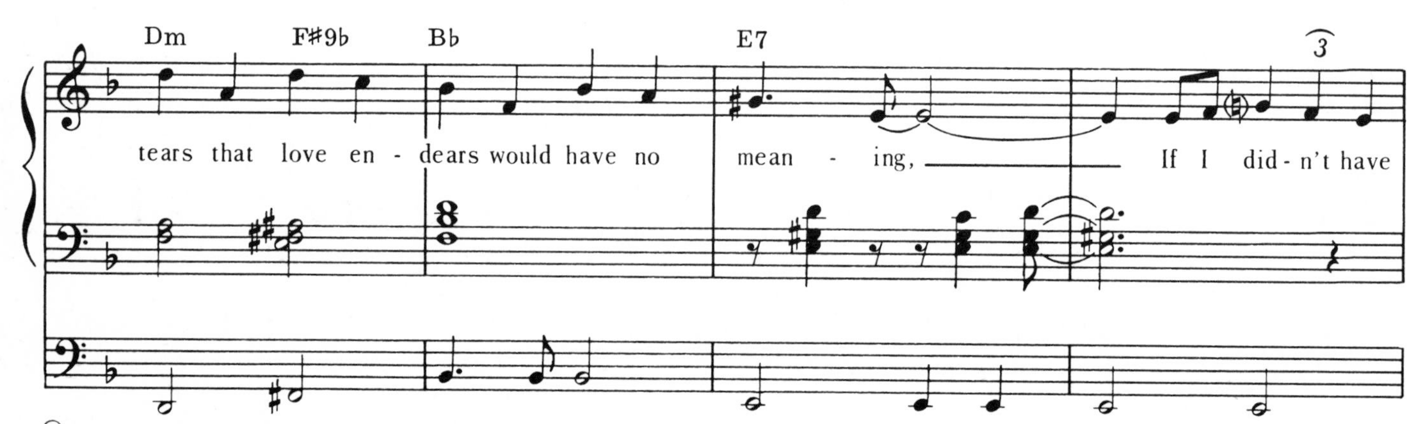

Gm6
Bb7
Gm6
A7
Dm
Dm(maj7)
you to keep me dream - ing; At the close of each day
Dm7
Gm
Gm7
C9
F#o
When I'm With - out You, And my heart kneels to pray,
C7
C7+
F
A+7 (b9)
A7 (b9)
Dm
F#b9
Bb
I pray a - bout you; You take a star and lead it far a - way from
E7
Gm
Gm6
A7 G#o A7 Gm6 Dm Gm6 Dm
heav - en, And the star will be lost As I'm lost With out You.

Babalú

English Lyric by
BOB RUSSELL

Music by
MARGARITA LECUONA

SUGGESTED REGISTRATIONS

Single-Manual Organs
8' 4' I II III

Vibrato: On

Play: Upper & Lower

General Electronic & Pipe Organs
Upper: Flute 16' 8' 4' 2' Piccolo 2' Mixture 2'
Lower: Flute 8' 4' (or Solo 8' Melodia 8')
Pedal: 16 + 8
Vibrato: On

Drawbar Organs
Upper: 70 8706 004
Lower: (00) 6443 211 (0)
Pedal: 5 - (3)
Vibrato: On

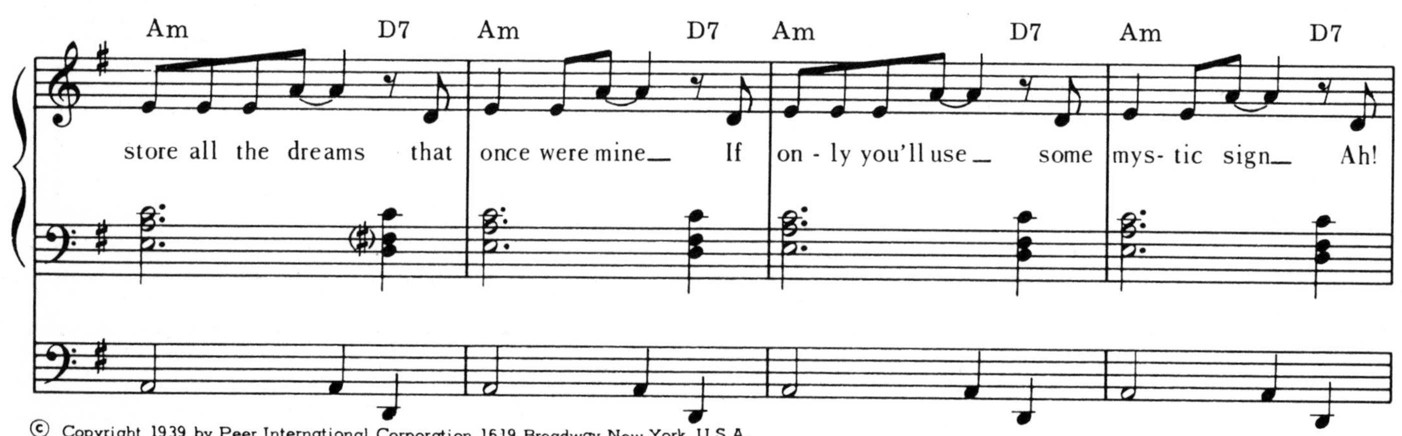

G
Do
D7
1 G6
D7
great Ba-ba-lu! Bring her back to me. Ah!
2 G6
D7
G
D7
G
me. Ba-ba-lu a-ye! Ba-ba-lu a-ye! Ba-ba-lu a-ye! Ba-ba-
D7
G
D7
G
-lu a-ye! Ba-ba-lu! a-ye! Ba-ba-lu! a-ye! Ba-ba-lu a-ye! Ba-ba-
D7
G
-lu a-ye! Ba-ba-lu a-ye! Ba-ba-lu a-ye!

Amor

English Lyric by
SUNNY SKYLAR

Music by
GABRIEL RUIZ

SUGGESTED REGISTRATIONS

Single-Manual Organs
8' 2' I II III V
Vibrato: On
Play: Upper & Lower

General Electronic & Pipe Organs
Upper: Strings 8'
Lower: Flute 8' 4' (or Melodia 8')
Pedal: 8'
Vibrato: On

Drawbar Organs
Upper: 00 4544 222
Lower: (00) 7756 310 (0)
Pedal: 3 - (2)
Vibrato: On

Bo C6 Bo C6 Em
I Have placed be - fore you. I can't find an-oth-er word with
B7 Em
mean - ing so clear, My lips try to whisp-er sweet-er things in your ear, But
G7 Bo E7 Am D7
some - how or oth - er noth - ing sounds quite so dear, As this soft car-ess - ing word I
G7 Dm7 G7 C
know. A - mor, A - mor, my love

G7
When you're a - way there is no day, And nights are lone - ly.
Dm
A - mor, A - mor, A - mor, my love Make life di-
G7 G7 C6 Ab7 C6
- vine. Say you'll be mine, And love me on - ly, A - mor,
Ab7 C
A - mor,

Sway

(QUIEN SERA)

English Lyric by
NORMAN GIMBEL

Music by
PABLO BELTRAN RUIZ

SUGGESTED REGISTRATIONS

Single-Manual Organs
8' 2' I II V

Vibrato: On

Play: Upper & Lower

General Electronic & Pipe Organs
Upper: Flute 8' Trumpet 8' Strings 8'
Lower: Flute 8' (or Melodia 8') Diapason 8'
Pedal: 8
Vibrato: On

Drawbar Organs
Upper: 00 8843 440
Lower: (00) 5404 000 (0)
Pedal: 4 - (2)
Vibrato: On

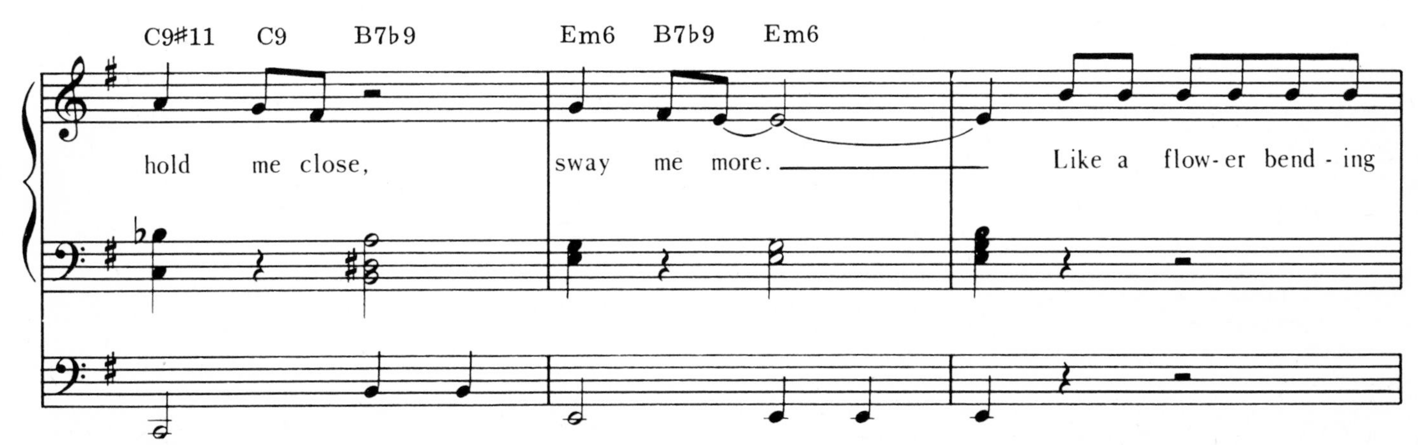

F#o B7 F#o B7 Em
in the breeze, bend with me, sway with ease,
C9#11 C9 B9 C9#11 C9 B7♭9
When we dance you have a way with me, stay with me,
Em6 B7♭9 Em6 G6 B♭o D7
sway with me, Oth - er dan - cers may be on the floor,
G
I got eyes dear to see on - ly you, On - ly you have that

B7
D#o
B7
Em
C9
B7♭9
mag - ic tech-nique,
when we sway I grow
weak.
Em
F#o
B7
F#o
B7
I can hear the sound of
vi - o - lins,
long be - fore
Em
C9#11
C9
B9
C9#11
C9
B7♭9
it be- gins,
Make me thrill as on- ly
you know how,
sway me smooth,
Em6
B7♭9
Em6
C
B7
Em
sway me now.
Sway me smooth, sway me
now.

English Lyric by
DAVID PALMER

Echo of a Serenade

(TE QUIERO DIJISTE)

Music by
MARIA GREVER

SUGGESTED REGISTRATIONS

Single-Manual Organs
8' 4' 2' I II
Vibrato: On
Play: Upper & Lower

General Electronic & Pipe Organs
Upper: Flute 16' 8' 4' 2' Trumpet 8'
Lower: Flute 8' 4' Diapason 8'
Pedal: 16 + 8
Vibrato: On

Drawbar Organs
Upper: 86 8757 234
Lower: (00) 8763 321 (0)
Pedal: 6 - (4)
Vibrato: On

Gm C7 F B♭o F F7 B♭ D7
mus - ic While a gyp - sy played Thro' the years I've wan - dered
G G♯o Am C6 Am6 D7 ten. Gm Gm7 Gm6 A7 Dm7 G9
Dream-ing of you dar - ling Pray- ing you'll re - mem - ber Love will nev-er
C7 B♭6 B♭m6 C7 F B♭m6 F
fade Liv-ing with a mem - 'ry Hearing in my rev - 'rie
Dm7 Gm G7 C7 F B♭9 F
Just the sad sweet Ech - o of a Ser- en - ade.

Perfidia

English Lyric by
MILTON LEEDS

Music by
ALBERTO DOMINGUEZ

SUGGESTED REGISTRATIONS

Single-Manual Organs
8' 2' I II III V
Vibrato: On
Play: Upper & Lower

General Electronic & Pipe Organs
Upper: Strings 8'
Lower: Flute 8' 4' (or Melodia 8')
Pedal: 8'
Vibrato: On

Drawbar Organs
Upper: 00 4544 222
Lower: (00) 7756 310 (0)
Pedal: 3 - (2)
Vibrato: On

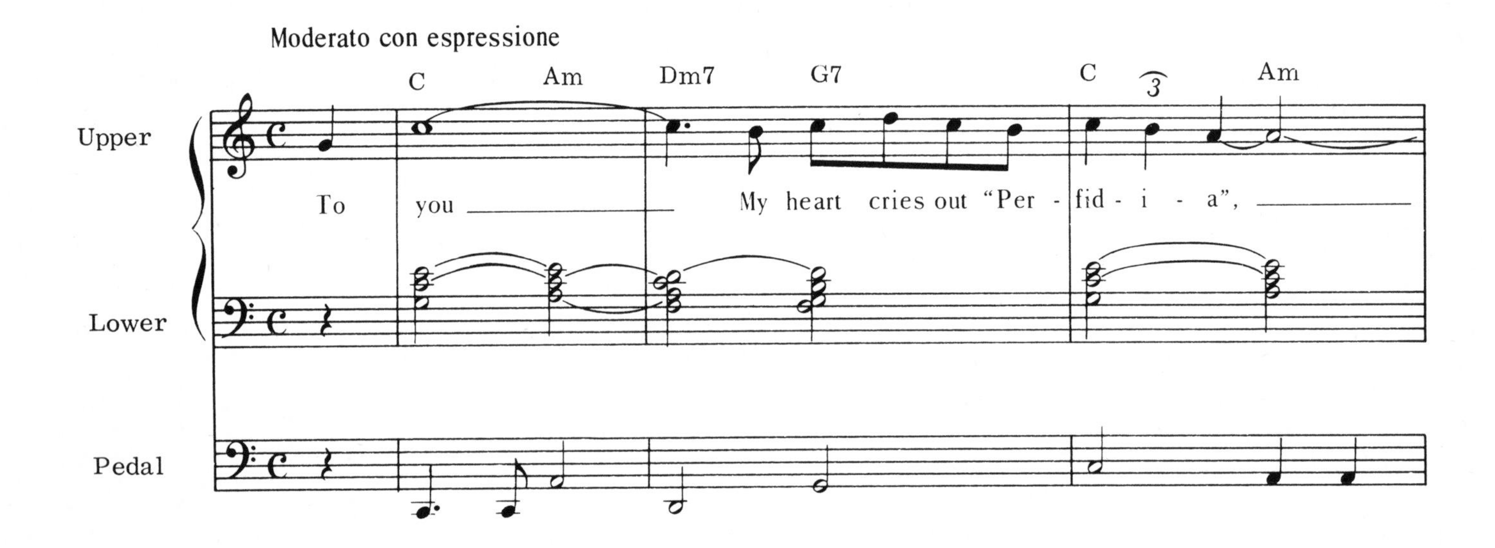

E7
G7
C
Am
Dm7
G7
arms. Your eyes are ech - o - ing "Per -
C
Am
Dm
G7
C
Am
- fid - i - a" For - get - ful of our pro - mise of love, You're
Dm7
F7-5
E7
shar - ing an - oth - er's charms. With a
Dm6
sad la - ment, my dreams have fad - ed like a bro - ken mel - o -

E7
Dm6
- dy; While the gods of love look down and laugh at
E
Dm7 Fm6 G7
what ro - man - tic fools we mor - tals be. And
C Am Dm7 G7 C Am Dm G7
now I know my love was not for you. And so I'll take it
C Am Dm7 G7 C Ab7 C6
back with a sigh, per - fid - i - ous one good - bye.

Come Closer To Me

(ACÉRCATE MÁS)

English Lyric by
AL STEWART

Music by
OSVALDO FARRES

SUGGESTED REGISTRATION

Single-Manual Organ
8' 4' I II V
Vibrato: On
Play: Upper & Lower

General Electronic & Pipe Organs
Upper: Flute 8' 4' 2' Quint, Nazard
Lower: Flute 8' 4' Diapason 8'
Pedal: 16 - 8
Vibrato: On

Drawbar Organs
Upper: 68 0060 066
Lower: (00) 6544 322 (0)
Pedal: 5 - (3)
Vibrato: On

tacet
Dm7 G7 Gm7 C7 Fmaj7 G#o
gain, And life will be di - vine; Come clos-er my dear, so I can
Gm C7 F C7 Fmaj7 G#o Gm C7
hear mus-ic in my heart; I've wait-ed so long to hear the song that your love will
F F7 Bb Bb6 Bbm6 Fsus Bb F D7+
start: Dar-ling I'll a - dore you, Live my life just for you, All I ask is
G9 C7 F Bo F6
this please give me one more kiss, and whis-per you'll be mine.

Guantanamera

Words & Music by
RAMON ESPIGUL

SUGGESTED REGISTRATIONS

Single-Manual Organs
8' 2' I III
Vibrato: On
Play: Upper & Lower

General Electronic & Pipe Organs
Upper: Flute 8' 4'
Lower: Diapason 8'
Pedal: 8'
Vibrato: On

Drawbar Organs
Upper: 60 8808 000
Lower: (00) 5554 433 (1)
Pedal: 4 - (2)
Vibrato: On

F Bb C7 F Bb C7
y yo de con - for - mi - dad
Es de rocul ual quie - ra su- er te
F Bb C7 F Bb C7
A - si que mi cuer poi ner - te
Lo lle - ven al cam - po san - to.
F Bb C7 F Bb F Bb
A - lli yo no quie - ro llan - to
quie - ro pa - ra Guan - ta - na - me - ra
C7 F Bb C7 F Bb C7
Gua - ji - ra Guan - tan - na me - ra
Guan - ta - na - me - ra.

Angelitos Negros

Words by
ANDRÉS ELOY BLANCO

(CANCIÓN MORUNA)

Music by
MANUEL ALVAREZ MACISTE

SUGGESTED REGISTRATIONS

Single-Manual Organs
8' I II III
Vibrato: On
Play: Upper & Lower

General Electronic & Pipe Organs
Upper: Flute 16' 8' 4' 2' Piccolo 2'
Lower: Flute 8' 4' Diapason 8'
Pedal: 8'
Vibrato: On

Drawbar Organs
Upper: 70 8706 004
Lower: (00) 5555 311 (0)
Pedal: 5 - (3)
Vibrato: On

E7 Dm6 E7 Dm6
ne - gros que tam-bien se van al cie - lo to - dos los ne - gri - tos
E7 Dm6 E7
bue - nos. Pin - tor si pin - tas con a - mor? por
Am G
que des- pre - cias su co - lor si - sa bes que enel
Dm6 B7♭5 E7
cie lo tam - bien los quie - re Dios Pin -

Am G Dm6 E7
- tor de San - tos de al - co - ba si tie - nes al -ma en el cuer - po por
Dm6 E7 Dm6 E7
que al pin - tar en tus cua - dros te ol vi das - te de los ne - gros
Am6 G Dm6 E7
3
Siem - pre que pin - tas li - gle - sias pin - tas an - ge - li - tos be - llos
Dm6 Eb9 E7 F7 E7 Am6 B9 E7 A6
pe - ro nun - ca te a - cor - das - te de pin - tar un an - gel ne - gro.

La Bamba

Adapted & Arranged by
LUIS MARTINEZ SERRANO

SUGGESTED REGISTRATIONS

Single-Manual Organs

8' 2' I II III

Vibrato: On
Play: Upper & Lower

General Electronic & Pipe Organs

Upper: Flute 8' 4' 2' Quint Nazard
Lower: Flute 8' 4' Diapason 8'
Pedal: 8'
Vibrato: On

Drawbar Organs

Upper: 60 8066 005

Lower: (00) 4433 220 (0)
Pedal: 4 - (2)
Vibrato: On

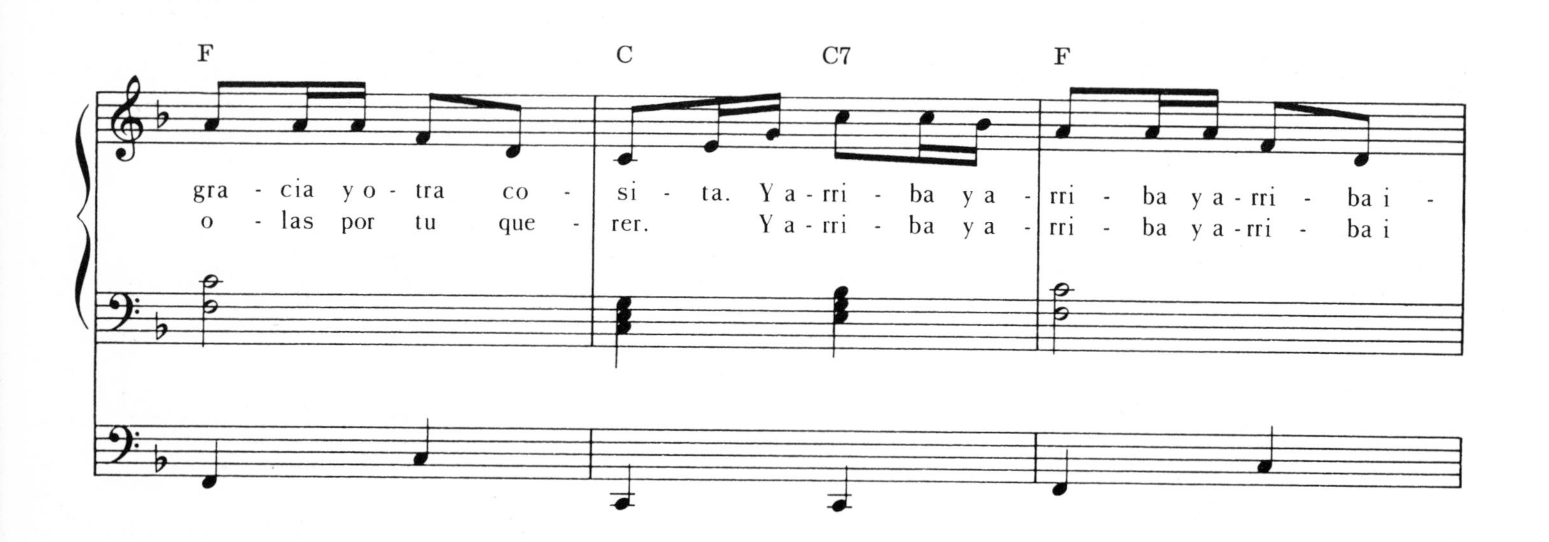

C7
F
C7
re; yo no soy ma - ri - ne - ro, por - ti se - re.
re; yo no soy ma - ri - ne - ro, por - ti se - re.
C7
C9
C7
C7
Yo no soy ma - ri - ne - ro, por ti se - re pe - ro a rri - ba y a -
F
C7
C9
C7
- rri - ba y a - rri - ba i re, yo no soy ma - ri - ne - ro por ti se -
C7
F
re, pe - ro a rri - ba y a - rri - ba y a - rri - ba i - re.

Be Mine Tonight

(NOCHE DE RONDE

Words by
SUNNY SKYLAR

Music by
MARIA TERESA LARA

SUGGESTED REGISTRATIONS

Single-Manual Organs
8' II
Vibrato: On
Play: Upper & Lower

General Electronic & Pipe Organs
Upper: Flute 8' 4' 2'
Lower: Flute 8' 4' (or Melodia 8')
Pedal: 16 + 8
Vibrato: On

Drawbar Organs
Upper: 73 5014 002
Lower: (00) 2564 422 (2)
Pedal: 4 - (2)
Vibrato: On

C6
C
Cmaj7
C6
- night. Pro - mise this, my own, be - fore the night has flown, You'll tell me that you
C
C7
C7+
F
A7
Dm
care; And hold me tight; Whis - per
Fm
Ab
Cm
G7
love words, oh, so ten - der, Give your kiss - es in sur -
Cm
G7+
Cm
Ab7
Cm6/9
- ren - der, Let your heart be mine to - night.

Maria Elena

English Lyric by
S. K. RUSSELL

Music by
LORENZO BARCELATA

SUGGESTED REGISTRATIONS

Single-Manual Organs
8' I II III IV
Vibrato: On
Play: Upper & Lower

General Electronic & Pipe Organs
Upper: Flute 16' 8' 4' 2'
Lower: Flute 8' 4' Diapason 8'
Pedal: 16' 8'
Vibrato: On

Drawbar Organs
Upper: 60 8806 004
Lower: (00) 6504 032 (2)
Pedal: 6 – (3)
Vibrato: On

C Tacet C C Dm
-bove a sigh Ma-ri-ae-le-na Say that we will nev-er part
G7 E7 Am
Ma-ri-ae-le-na Take me to your heart A
F Fm A♭7 C
love like mine is great e-nough for two To share this
D7 G7 C Fm C
love is real-ly all I ask of you my love.

Always In My Heart

Lyric by
KIM GANNON

(SIEMPRE EN MI CORAZON)

Music by
ERNESTO LECUONA

SUGGESTED REGISTRATIONS

Single-Manual Organs
8' 4' 2' I II
Vibrato: On
Play: Upper & Lower

General Electronic & Pipe Organs
Upper: Flute 16' 8' 4' 2' Trumpet 8'
Lower: Flute 8' 4' Diapason 8'
Pedal: 16 + 8
Vibrato: On

Drawbar Organs
Upper: 86 8757 234
Lower: (00) 8763 321 (0)
Pedal: 6 - (4)
Vibrato: On

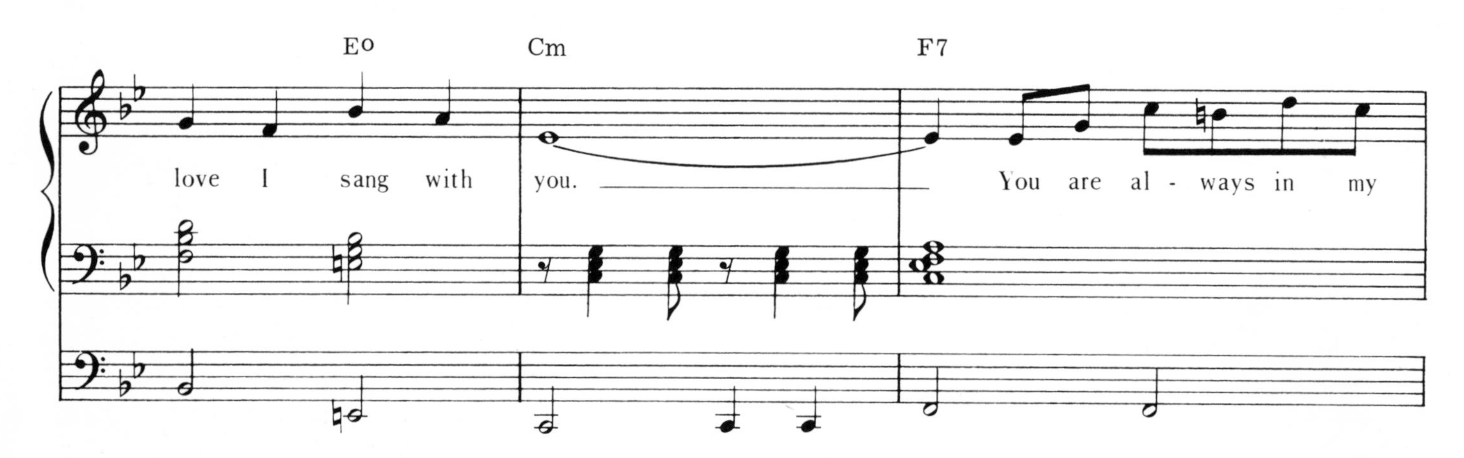

Cm7
Ebm6
F7
heart and when skies a - bove are grey
Cm7
F7
Eo
I re - mem-ber that you care and then and there the sun breaks
Bb
F+
thru. Just be - fore I go to sleep
Bb
F+7
Bb
F+
Bb
there's a ren - dez - vous I keep and the dream I al - ways

Fm6 G7
meet helps me for - get we're far a - part
Cm
I don't know ex - act - ly when dear but I'm sure we'll meet a -
Ebm6
Bb
Bbo
F7
A
gain dear and my dar - ling till we do
F7
Bb
you are al - ways in my heart.

English Lyric by
NORMAN GIMBEL

Mas Que Nada
(SAY NO MORE)

Music by
JORGE BEN

SUGGESTED REGISTRATIONS

Single-Manual Organs
8' 4' I II III V

Vibrato: On

Play: Upper & Lower

General Electronic & Pipe Organs
Upper: Flute 8' 4' 2' Piccolo 2' Mixture 2'
Lower: Flute 8' 4' (or Solo 8' Melodia 8') Diapason 8'
Pedal: 8'
Vibrato: On

Drawbar Organs
Upper: 80 8736 567

Lower: (00) 5544 220 (0)

Pedal: 6 - (3)
Vibrato: On

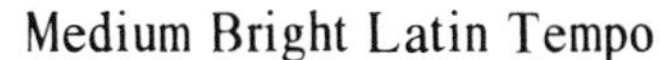

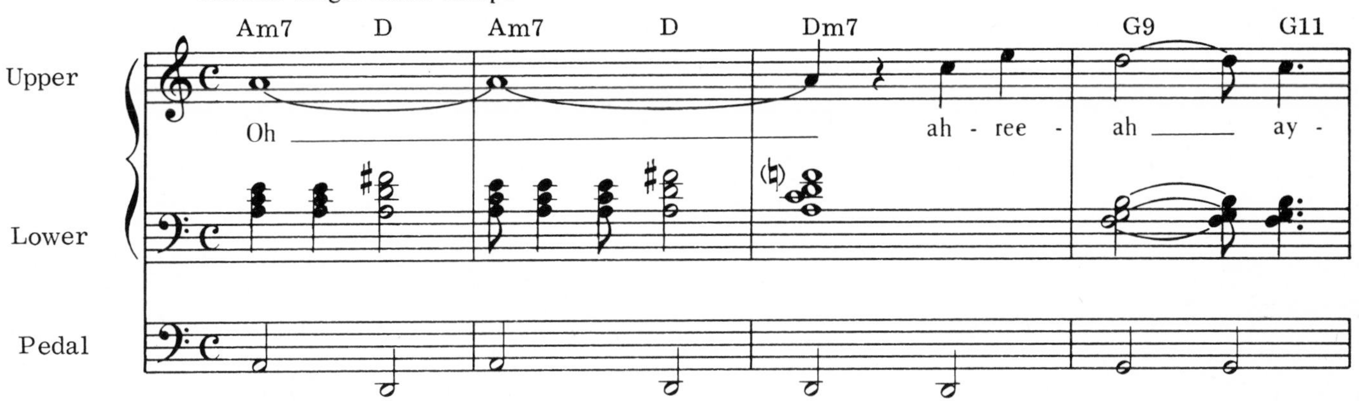

Am D Am E9# E9♭ Am Am7 E9# E9♭ Am
-bah Mas que na — da. say no more, my dear, for when I hear a sam-
E9# Am Am
-ba, — Some-thing deep in the heart of me stirs, — and mas que
E7 Am D(E Root) A D(E Root)
na - da, say — no more! — They took
Dm7 G7 C6 Cmaj7
sam - ba — and mixed — it with ma - ra - ca - tu. —

C6
D
Dm6 Dm(sus G) E7 E9#
And the ma - gic way it gets me, it's got - ta get to you,
Am
Am(+9)
E9#
E9b
Am
Am7
Mas que na da! For
E9#
E9b
Am
E9#
more than an - y - thing I love the sam - ba, The beat I can't ig -
Am
E7
Am
D(E Root)
- nore, Let me dance and say no more.

El Cumbanchero

English Words by
JOE CRAYHON &
GEORGE WILLIAMS

Music by
RAFAEL HERNANDEZ

SUGGESTED REGISTRATIONS

Single-Manual Organs
8' I II
Vibrato: Off

Play: Upper & Lower

General Electronic & Pipe Organs
Upper: Clarinet 8' (or 16') Trumpet 8'
Lower: Flute 8' (or Melodia 8')
Diapason 8'
Bassoon 8' (or Viola 8')
Pedal: 8'
Vibrato: Off

Drawbar Organs
Upper: 00 8373 441
Lower: (00) 6443 423 (0)
Pedal: 4 - (2)
Vibrato: Off

G7
play,
run,
with a la - dy in his
to an - oth - er la - dy's
Cm
arms.
arms.
1
2. El
2
C7
Girls
don't be - lieve that
he could tell a
(Vibrato)
Fm
lie
Ay ay
ay
Fm
All
Fm
of them think that
he's their spe - cial
G7
guy,
hear 'em

Cm
cry, Hey cum-ba, cum-ba, cum-ba, cum-ban-che-ro
Vibrato off
Cm
The sen-o-ri-tas wait for his bo-le-ro, But El
Bb Ab Eb Fm Cm Fo Ao
Cum-ban-che-ro takes his time so they will have to stand in line to
G7 Cm G7 Cm
dance In El Cum-ban-che-ro's arms.

Frenesi

English Words by
RAY CHARLES &
S. K. RUSSELL

Music by
ALBERTO DOMINGUEZ

SUGGESTED REGISTRATIONS

Single-Manual Organs
8' 2' I II III V
Vibrato: On
Play: Upper & Lower

General Electronic & Pipe Organs
Upper: Strings 8'
Lower: Flute 8' 4' (or Melodia 8')
Pedal: 8'
Vibrato: On

Drawbar Organs
Upper: 00 4544 222
Lower: (00) 7756 310 (0)
Pedal: 3 - (2)
Vibrato: On

Am
D7
Do
D7
Am
D7
Do
caught my eye I stood en-chant-ed as she wan-der'd by
D7
G
D7
And nev-er know-ing that it came from me I gent-ly sigh'd Fren-e-
G
G Tacet
B
-si'. She stopped and rais'd her eyes to mine
Am
B
Her lips just plea-ded to be kiss'd Her eyes were soft as can-dle-shine

C A7 D7 Tacet
So how was I to re - sist? And now with-out a heart to
Am D7 Do D7 Am D7 Do
call my own A great-er hap-pi - ness I've nev - er known
D7 G Am D7
Be-cause her kiss-es are for me a - lone Who would - n't say 'Fren-e -
G C D7 G
- si'? Who would - n't say 'Fren- e - si?.

Cuanto Le Gusta

Words by
RAY GILBERT

Music by
GABRIEL RUIZ

SUGGESTED REGISTRATIONS

Single-Manual Organs
8' I II III
Vibrato: On
Play: Upper & Lower

General Electronic & Pipe Organs
Upper: Flute 16' 8' 4' 2' Piccolo 2'
Lower: Flute 8' 4' Diapason 8'
Pedal: 8'
Vibrato: On

Drawbar Organs
Upper: 70 8706 004
Lower: (00) 5555 311 (0)
Pedal: 5 - (3)
Vibrato: On

D7
where we go - in',M And what-a we gon - na do? We're on our way to
G
"some-where", the three of us and you. What - 'll we see there,
D7
who will be there, What - 'll be the big sur - prise? There
may be se - no - ri - tas with dark and flash - ing

G D7 G D7
eyes, We're on our way, Pack up your pack,
And if we stay, we won't come back,
G Dm
How can we
E7 Am Cm6
go, We have-n't got a dime, But we're
G D7 G Am7 G D7
go - in', And we're gon-na have a hap - py time.

Cielito Lindo

(VALS)

Words & Music by
QUIRINO MENDOZA

SUGGESTED REGISTRATIONS

Single-Manual Organs
8' 4' I II III
Vibrato: On
Play: Upper & Lower

General Electronic & Pipe Organs
Upper: Flute 16' 8' 4' 2' Quint
Lower: Flute 8' (Melodia) Diapason 8'
Pedal: 8'
Vibrato: On

Drawbar Organs
Upper: 80 8757 234
Lower: (00) 7665 211 (0)
Pedal: 5 - (3)
Vibrato: On

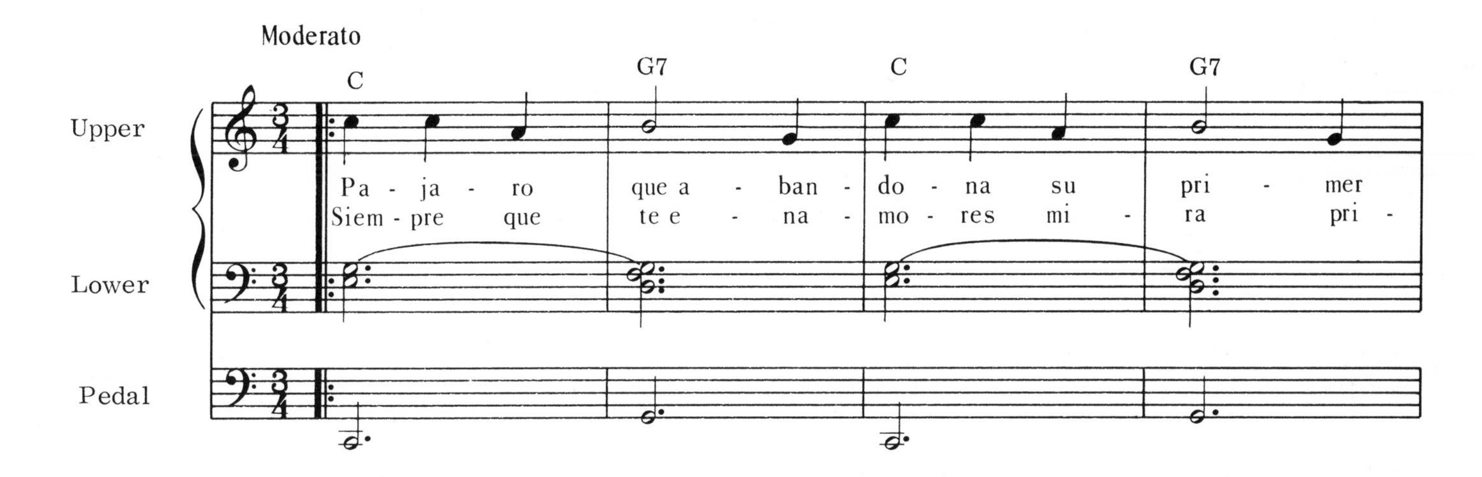

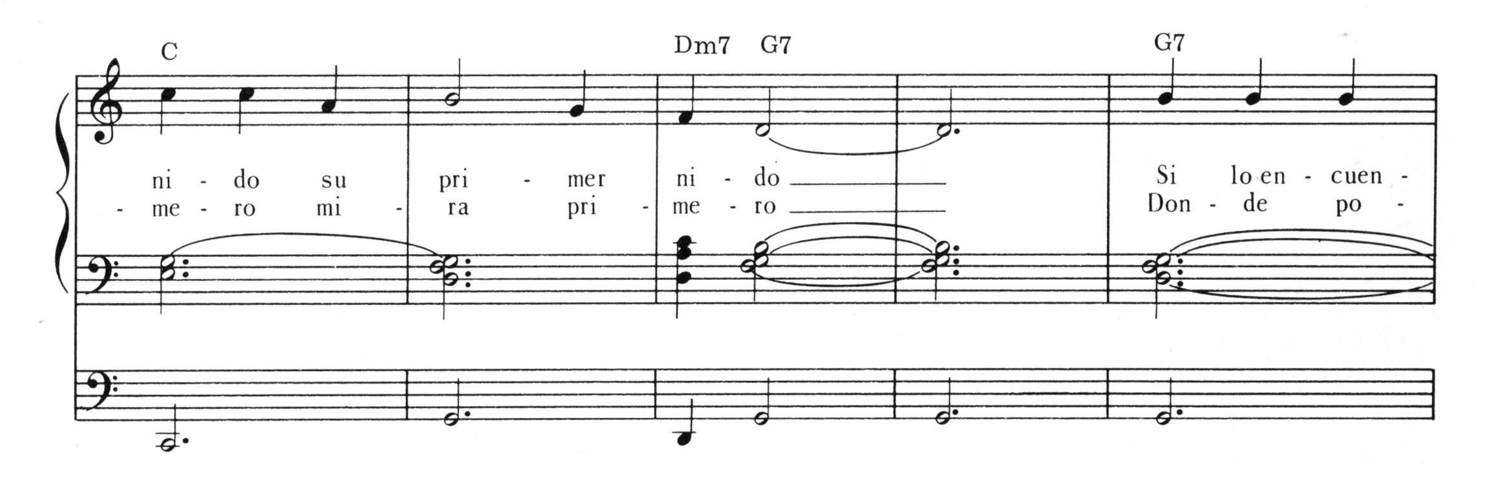

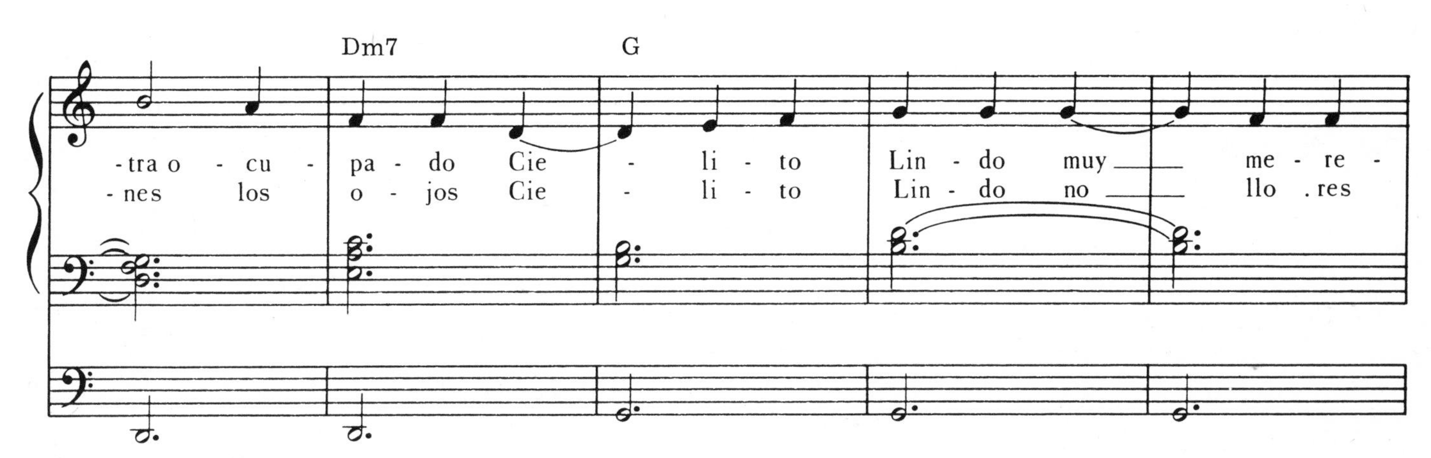

C
C
C7
C+ 7
F
- ci - do
lue - go
. Ay
ay
ay
ay!
Dm
Dm7
G7
Dm7
C
can - ta y no llo - res por -
C
Dm
Dm7
G7
- que can - tan - do se a - le - gran Cie - li - to Lin - do - los
1 C
G7
2 C
co - ra - zo - nes
zo - nes.

Perhaps, Perhaps, Perhaps

(QUIZAS, QUIZAS, QUIZAS)

English Words by
JOE DAVIS

Music by
OSVALDO FARRES

SUGGESTED REGISTRATIONS

Single-Manual Organs
8' I II V
Vibrato: On
Play: Upper & Lower

General Electronic & Pipe Organs
Upper: Flute 8' 4' 2' Piccolo 2'
Lower: Flute 8' 4' Diapason 8'
Pedal: 8'
Vibrato: On

Drawbar Organs
Upper: 40 8060 066
Lower: (00) 6543 000 (0)
Pedal: 4 - (2)
Vibrato: On

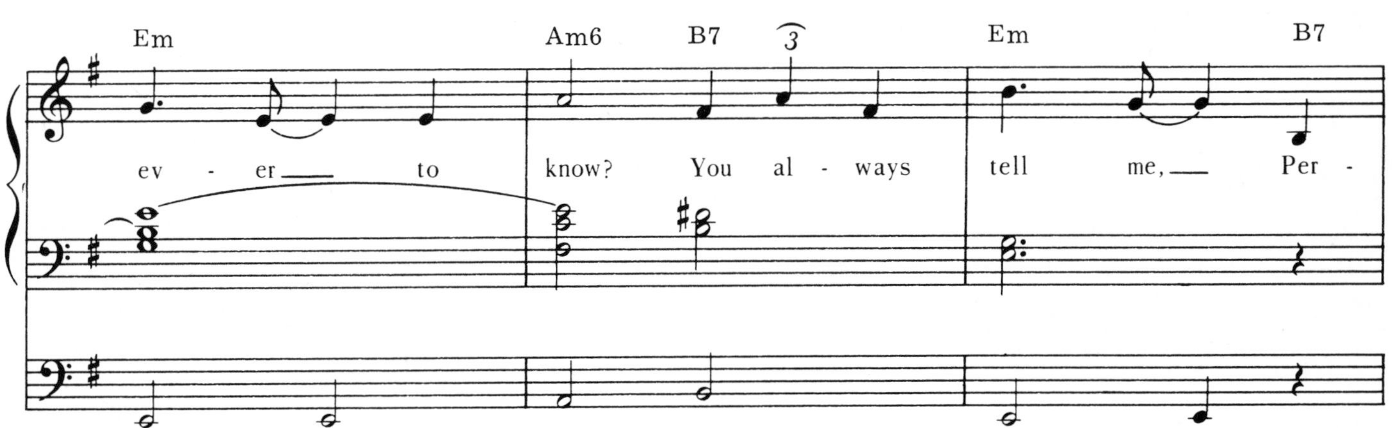

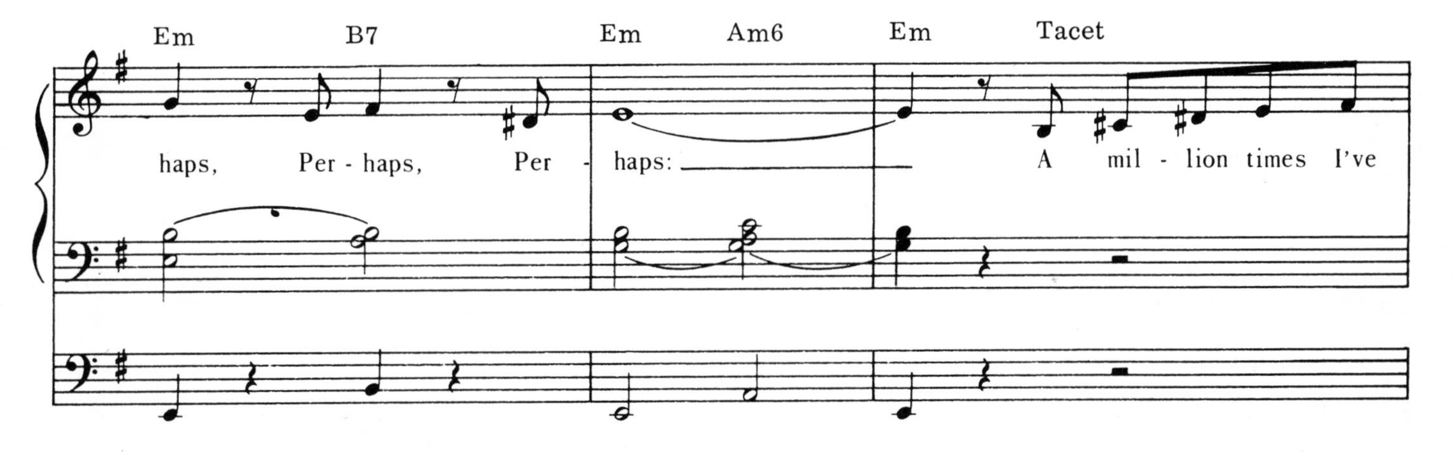

Em Am6 B7 3 Em
asked you, and then I ask you ov - er a -
Am6 B7 3 Em B7 Em B7
gain, You on - ly an - swer Per - haps, Per - haps, Per -
Em Am6 Em A6 B7 A6
- haps; If you can't make your mind up, we'll
B7 E A6
nev - er get start - ed; And I don't want to

B7 A6 B7 E
wind up — be - ing part - ed, — bro - ken heart - ed; —
Em Am6 B7 3
— So, if you real - ly love me, — say "yes," But if you
Em Am6 B7 3 Em B7
don't, dear, — con - fess, And please don't tell me, — Per -
Em B7 Em Am6 Em
- haps, Per - haps, Per - haps. —

Sweet And Gentle

(ME LO DIJO ADELA)

English Words by
GEORGE THORN

Music by
OTILIO PORTAL

SUGGESTED REGISTRATIONS

Single-Manual Organs
8' 2' I II III V
Vibrato: On
Play: Upper & Lower

General Electronic & Pipe Organs
Upper: Strings 8'
Lower: Flute 8' 4' (or Melodia 8')
Pedal: 8'
Vibrato: On

Drawbar Organs
Upper: 00 4544 222
Lower: (00) 7756 310 (0)
Pedal: 3 - (2)
Vibrato: On

D7
G
And now I'll nev-er be the
same! For I
have turned in-to a danc-ing cu-cu-
D7
Am7
D7
G
D7
Am7
C+
-ra-cha!
And my mu-chacha is to
blame.
How can I be
gen-tle,
Am7
D7
G
Gmaj7
G6
G
Am7
C+
Sweet and sen-ti-
mental,
While the cha-cha's
playing,
Am7
D7
G
And my heart is
sway-ing!
I find that
I am ev-en danc-ing when I'm

D7 Am7 D7 G
walk-ing! I'm haunt-ed by that cha-cha beat! I hear the
D7 Am7 D7 G D7
rhy-thm start whenev-er we are talk-ing, I do the cha-cha in my sleep.
Am7 C+ Am7 D7 G Gmaj7
Please be Sweet and Gen-tle, Treat me sen-ti - mental,
G6 G Am7 D7 D7 Am7 D7 G6 F#6 G6
For I'm temp-ra - men-tal, When I'm do - ing the cha - cha with you!

Lyric by
RAYMOND KARL
& CHARLIE TOWNE

Mambo Jambo

(QUE RICO EL MAMBO)

Music by
PEREZ PRADO

SUGGESTED REGISTRATIONS

Single-Manual Organs
8' I II

Vibrato: Off

Play: Upper & Lower

General Electronic & Pipe Organs
Upper: Clarinet 8' (or 16')
Trumpet 8'
Lower: Flute 8' (or Melodia 8')
Diapason 8' Bassoon 8'
(or Viola 8')
Pedal: 8'
Vibrato: Off

Drawbar Organs
Upper: 00 8373 441

Lower: (00) 6443 423 (0)

Pedal: 4 - (2)
Vibrato: Off

Bright tempo

G7 G#o G7

Upper

Do it with some - one you mad - ly a - dore,
Lat - in A - mer - i - can kind of ro - mance,

Lower

Pedal

2
Cmaj7
C
G7
Here is the part where she'll want to be kissed.
Diff 'rent from an - y rhum - ba,
Bet - ter than an - y sam - ba,
Great - er than an - y tan - go,
Wild - er than an - y con - ga.
Fm
The min - ute that you be - gin,
It teach - es your heart the beat,
Vibrato on

C
You'll find it be - neath your skin,—
Then goes to your head and feet,—
Dm A7 Dm A7
Like the hoo - doo
Like a shak - er
F G7 F G7
of a voo - doo
of Ja - mai - ca
1 C
drum.
2
rum
You
C7
do the Mam - bo
do the Mam - bo
Vibrato off
F
Jam - bo;
Jam - bo;
Fmaj7
You
All
C7
dance
night
to break of
you hol - ler

F
1 F
2 F
day, day, day, day, You Ho - lay!
hey! hey!
Fm
C
You'll find at the break of day, Your heart has been
The mo - ment your love is found, The mo - ment your
Vibrato on
Dm A7 Dm A7 F G7 F G7
flown a - way; To a land where on - ly lov - ers
heart is bound, You will bless the Mam - bo Jam - bo
Vibrato off
1 C
2 C
dwell. Spell. (Uh - h - h - h)

Patricia, It's Patricia

Words by
BOB MARCUS

Music by
PEREZ PRADO

SUGGESTED REGISTRATIONS

Single-Manual Organs
8' I II

Vibrato: Off

Play: Upper & Lower

General Electronic & Pipe Organs
Upper: Clarinet 8' (or 16')
Trumpet 8'
Lower: Flute 8' (or Melodia 8')
Diapason 8' Bassoon 8'
(or Viola 8')
Pedal: 8'
Vibrato: Off

Drawbar Organs
Upper: 00 8373 441
Lower: (00) 6443 423 (0)
Pedal: 4 - (2)
Vibrato: Off

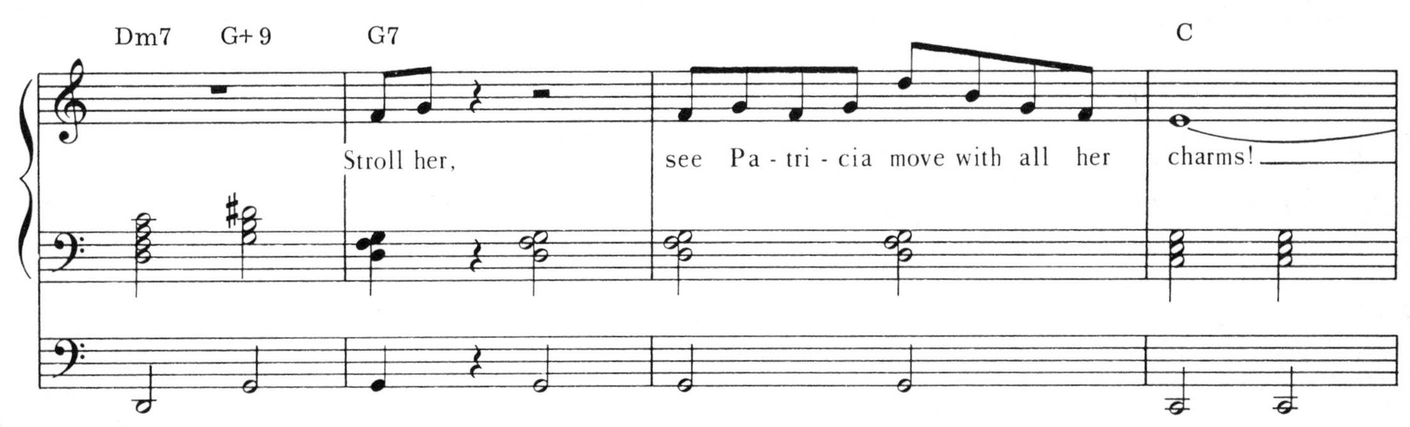

Dm7 G7
C
Heaven, that's where you'll be when she's in your arms!
Who took the Place of De De Di - nah? Pa - tri - cia!
And Peg-gy Sue is jeal-ous, too, of Pa - tri - cia!
G7
Dm7 G7
And when she's wear-ing her Bi - ki - ni,
Dm7 G7 C6
C
Her hips will have you hyp - no - tized!
Far off

G7
Dm7
G+9
in Ja - pan, they brag a - bout their Gei - sha,
G7
C
G+9
Who cares, 'long as Un - cle Sam has got Pa - tri - cia!
Dm7
G+9
C
Dm7
Eyes, that have a star - ry sort of gleam for
Vibrato on
G7
Dm7
G7
Dm7
G7
you. She is like a mil - lion dol - lar

Cmaj7
C
C6
C
dream come true!
Ev - 'ry - bod - y wish - es they could
Vib. Off
G9
steal her heart a - way, I guess,
G7
Dm7
G+
C6
There's so man - y try - in' but she nev - er, nev - er will say "yes"!
G+ 9
C
Kiss her and your lips will al - ways want Pa -

G7
Dm7
G+9
G7
-tri - cia!
Stroll her
see Pa - tri - cia move with all her
C
Dm7
G+9
charms.
C
G7
Dm7
G7
Far off
in Ja - pan, they brag a - bout their
Gei-sha,
C
G7
C
Who cares,
long as Un - cle Sam has got Pa - tri - cia!

Bluebird Of All My Dreams

(AZULÃO)

English Words by
ALAN MURRAY

Music by
JAYME OVALLE

SUGGESTED REGISTRATIONS

Single-Manual Organs
8' 4' 2' I II
Vibrato: On
Play: Upper & Lower

General Electronic & Pipe Organs
Upper: Flute 16' 8' 4' 2' Trumpet 8'
Lower: Flute 8' 4' Diapason 8'
Pedal: 16 + 8
Vibrato: On

Drawbar Organs
Upper: 86 8757 234
Lower: (00) 8763 321 (0)
Pedal: 6 - (4)
Vibrato: On

A7 Am7(5♭) D7 G Go D7 G
true is my lone - ly heart. Long is the part- ing, O
Go Am7 D7 G G7 C D11 D7
Blue -bird of all my dreams O find me my dar - ling,
G Go Am7 D7 G G7
Tell her I wait for the sound of your out - stretched wings. Soon
C E7♭9 E7 A7 Am7 5♭ D7 G
bring - ing her back to me, back to my hap - py heart.

In Old Lisbon

LISBOA ANTIGUA

Lyric by
HARRY DUPREE

Music by
RAUL PORTELA,
J. GALHARDO & A. DO VALE

SUGGESTED REGISTRATIONS

Single-Manual Organs
8' I II IV V
Vibrato: On
Play: Upper & Lower

General Electronic & Pipe Organs
Upper: Strings 8' Clarinet 8'
Lower: Flute 8' 4' (or Melodia 8')
Pedal: 8'
Vibrato: On

Drawbar Organs
Upper: 00 7787 753
Lower: (00) 6520 000 (0)
Pedal: 5 - (2)
Vibrato: On

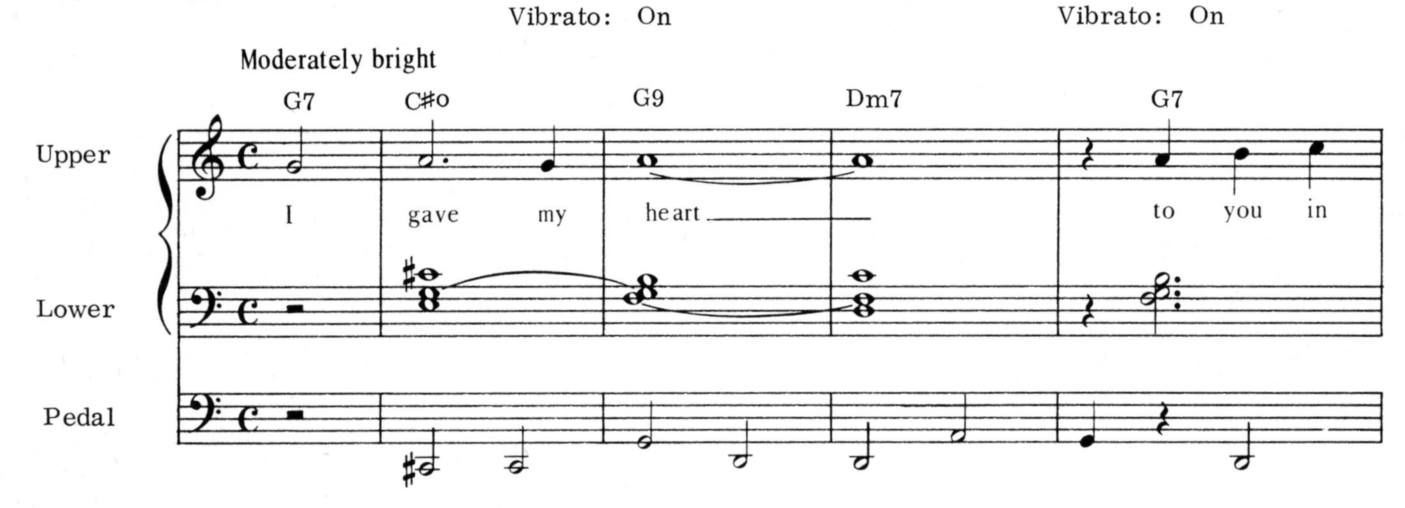

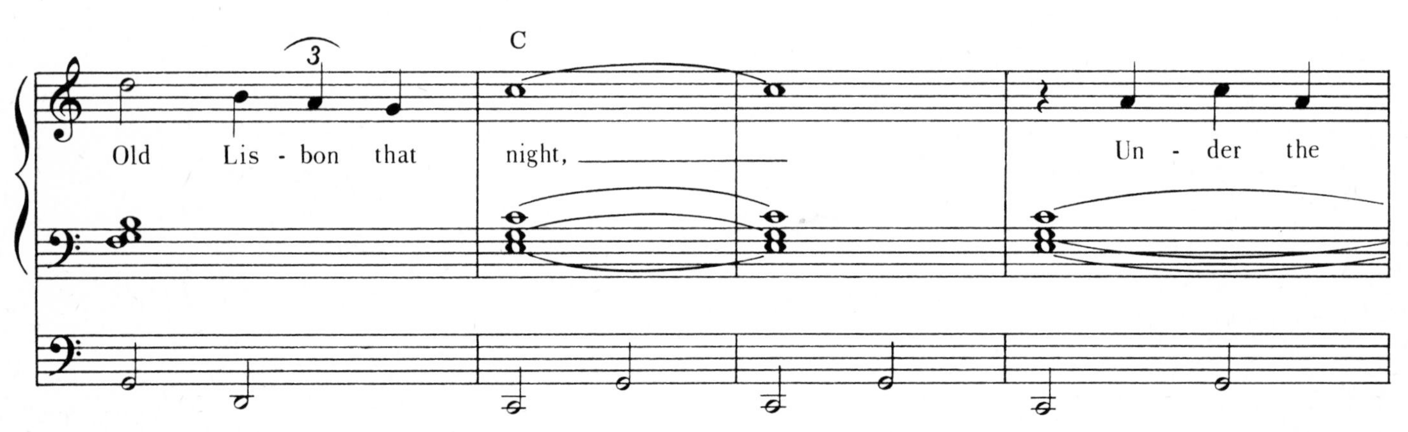

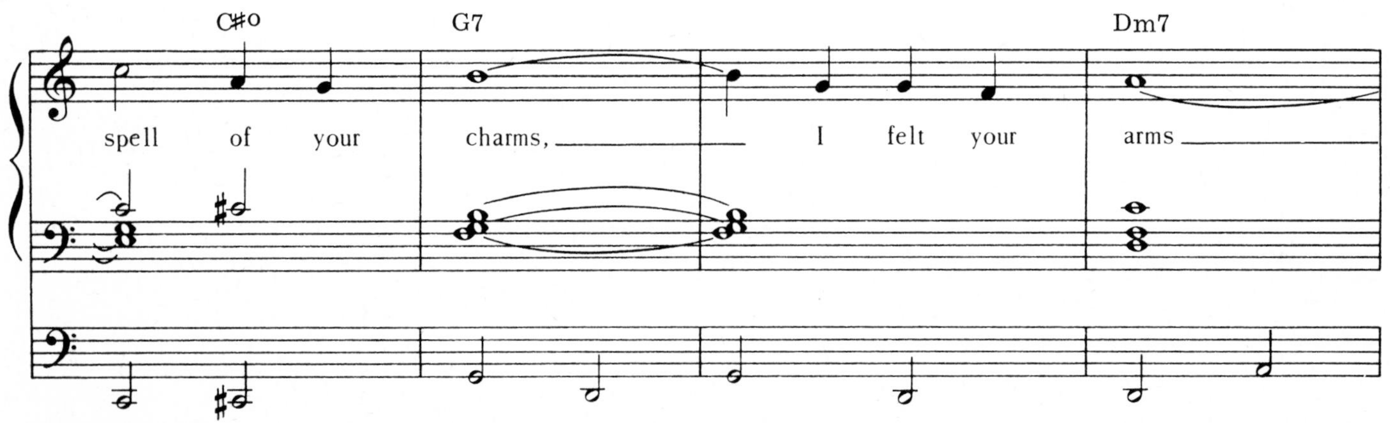

G7
C
C#o
Dm7
— hold me so
tight; ——
'Twas
heav - en ——
G7
C
— to find such
bliss in each
kiss; ——
I lost my
C#o
G7
Dm7
G7
C#o
G9
G7
heart but I
found one so
true, ——
In Old Lis - bon with
C
Bb
Fm
G7
Cm
you. ——
It hap - pened
one night in

G7 Dm7♭5 G7 Cm
Por - tu - gal Lis-bon was gay in the moon-light,
Cm B♭ A♭
The stars were shin - ing a - bove when I found you, my
G7 Cm Dm7♭5
love; What is this strange - ness, this splen-dor,
G7 Cm G7 Cm G7 Cm
all this mys - t'ry that makes me sur - ren - der?

Tico-Tico

(TICO-TICO NO FUBA)

English Lyric by
ERVIN DRAKE

Music by
ZEQUINHA ABREU

SUGGESTED REGISTRATIONS

Single-Manual Organs
8' I II
Vibrato: Off

Play: Upper & Lower

General Electronic & Pipe Organs
Upper: Clarinet 8' (or 16') Trumpet 8'
Lower: Flute 8' (or Melodia 8')
Diapason 8' Bassoon 8'
(or Viola 8')
Pedal: 8'
Vibrato: Off

Drawbar Organs
Upper: 00 8373 441
Lower: (00) 6443 423 (0)
Pedal: 4 - (2)
Vibrato: Off

Bright Samba tempo

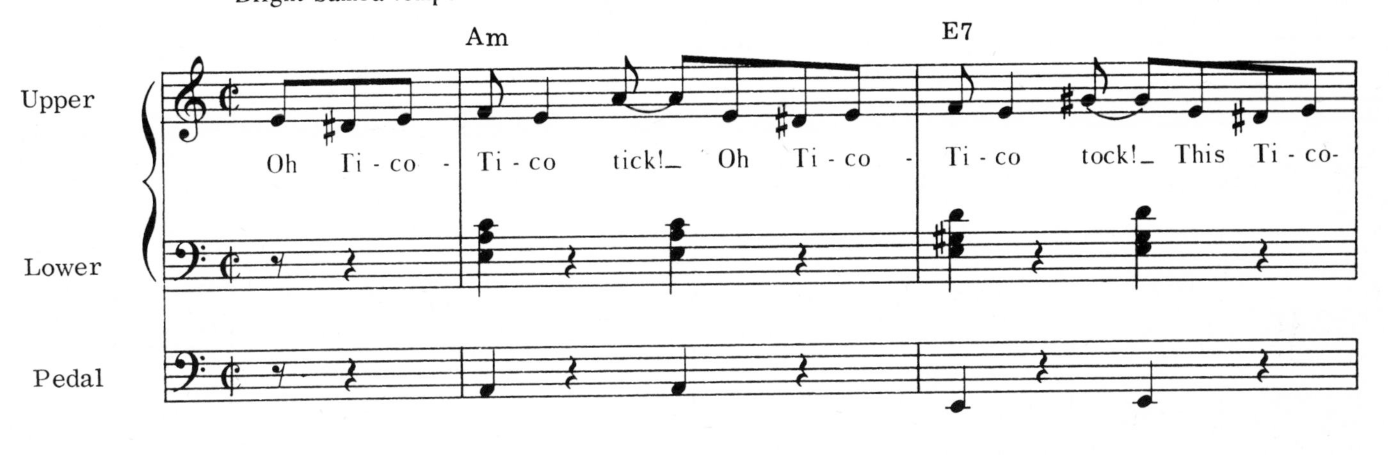

Am
E7
heav- y date_ a tete- a - tete at eight,_ so speak, oh Ti - co, tell me is it get - ting
Am
Dm
Am
late? If I'm on time: "Cuck- oo!"_ But if I'm late, "Woo - woo!"_ The one my
E7
Am
C
heart has gone to may not want to wait! For just a bir - die, and a bir - die who goes
Vibrato on
G7
C
no - where, He knows of ev - 'ry Lov-ers' Lane and how to go there; For in af -

A+
Dm
G7
fairs of the heart,_ my Ti - co's ter - ri - bly smart, He tells me: "Gent-ly, sen - ti - ment'ly at the
C
G7
C
G7
start!" Oh - oh, I hear my lit - tle Ti - co - Ti - co call - ing, Be-cause the
G7
C
Dm
Co
time is right and shades of night are fall - ing. I love that not - so-cuck-oo cuck-oo in the
Vibrato off
C
Dm7
G7
C
clock: Ti - co - Ti - co Ti - co Ti - co - Ti - co tock.

Eso Es El Amor

English Lyric by
SUNNY SKYLAR

(CHA CHA)

Words & Music by
PEPE IGLESIAS

SUGGESTED REGISTRATIONS

Single-Manual Organs
8' 4' 2' I II

Vibrato: On

Play: Upper & Lower

General Electronic & Pipe Organs
Upper: Flute 16' 8' 4' 2' Piccolo 2' Trumpet 8'
Lower: Flute 8' 4' Diapason 8' Bassoon 8'
Pedal: 16 + 8
Vibrato: On

Drawbar Organs
Upper: 80 8736 567
Lower: (00) 5544 220 (0)
Pedal: 6 - (3)
Vibrato: On

A7
Dm
moun-tain, the des-ert, the foun-tain, You're
A7
Dm
sweet-ness and de - sire, the wa-ter and the fire,
A7
Dm
Dm6
E - so Es El a - mor. Si Se - nor.
A7
A7♭9
A7
A7♭9
Dm6
When you hold me I hear the roar - ing of the o - cean,

A7
A7(9♭)
Si, si, si, si, si, si, si,
So en-fold me with all your love and your
Dm6
D7
D7♭9
de-vo-tion,
Si, si, si, si, si, si, si,
When you kiss me you
Gm6
al-ways set my heart on fi-re,
Si, si si si si si si
A7(♭9)
A+
Dm
Kiss me, kiss me, Es-o Es El A-mor.
Si Sig-nor.

Anna

(El N. Zumbon)

English Lyric by
WILLIAM ENGVICK

Music by
R. VATRO

SUGGESTED REGISTRATIONS

Single-Manual Organs
8' I II
Vibrato: Off

Play: Upper & Lower

General Electronic & Pipe Organs
Upper: Clarinet 8' (or 16') Trumpet 8'
Lower: Flute 8' (or Melodia 8')
Diapason 8' Bassoon 8'
(or Viola 8')
Pedal: 8'
Vibrato: Off

Drawbar Organs
Upper: 00 8373 441
Lower: (00) 6443 423 (0)
Pedal: 4 - (2)
Vibrato: Off

D7
got, makes you think that it's spring when it's
G
not. Take a
look, take a look and you'll
D7
say, "What a
Am7 D7
day! What a day!" An - na's
G
day!"
D7
An - na's
G
got that cer - tain some -
D7
thing that tops the
Vibrato: On
G
list, The
B♭°
kind of lips_ you'll nev -
D7
er re - sist,
They've got

G
D7
to be kissed,
They've got
to be kissed,
right a -
G
Am7
D9
D7
way!
When - ev - er
An - na's a - round
you'll hear a
G
B♭o
Am7
D7
Am7
D7
sor - row-ful sound,
That sound that
heart's are mak - in'
when they break in two.
G
Am7
D9
D7
The fel - las
look and they fall,
But she can't

G Bb° Am7 D7 Am7 D7
help it at all, It's just as nat - 'ral as the sky is when it's blue.
G D7 G D7
An - na smiles and all the world is a ros - y
Vibrato off
G Bb° D7
mist, And soon your heart - 'll start to in - sist She's got
G D7 G
to be kissed, She's got to be kissed right a - way!

Be True To Me

Song Version of "CARNAVALITO"

Words by
GEORGE THORN

Music by
EDMUNDO P. ZALDIVAR

SUGGESTED REGISTRATIONS

Single-Manual Organs
8' 4' 2' I II

Vibrato: On

Play: Upper & Lower

General Electronic & Pipe Organs
Upper: Flute 8' 4' 2' Mixture 2' (or Twelfth) Clarinet 8' (or 16') Quint
Lower: Flute 8' 4' (or Solo 8' Melodia 8')
Pedal: 8'
Vibrato: On

Drawbar Organs
Upper: 73 5014 002
Lower: (00) 4131 221 (0)
Pedal: 5 – (3)
Vibrato: On

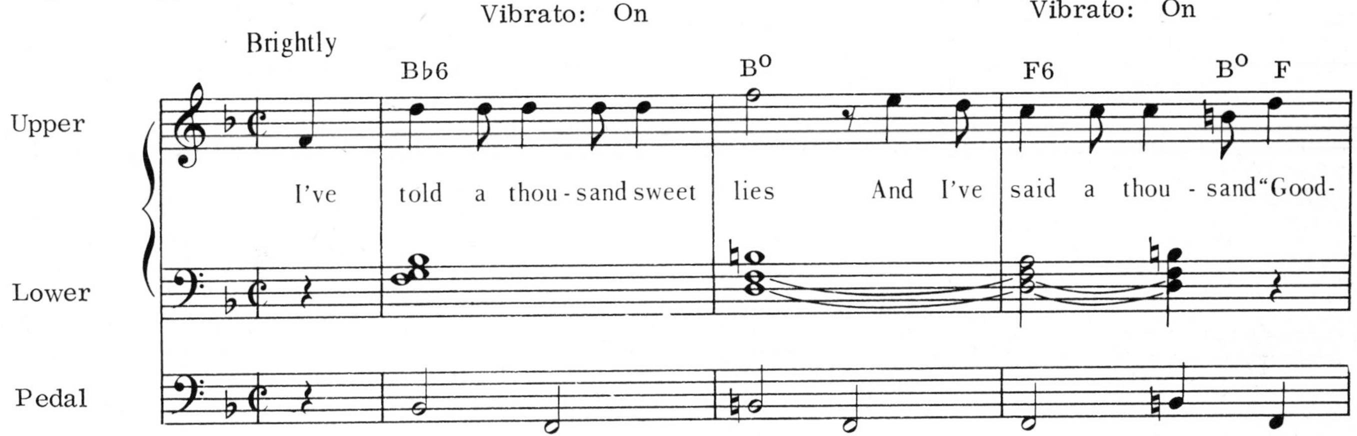

Gm9
C7
F6
Gm9
C7
eyes like the deep blue sea,
Hair made of gold, and
Gm9
3
C7
Gm9
Bb13
A7+
Dm
F7
lips that are bold, Who'll al - ways be true to me. I've
Bb6
G7
C7
F6
been through the world giv - ing my dreams a chance,
F7
Bb6
G7
C7
Fmaj 9
I've known man - y girls, But nev - er real ro - mance.

F6 Gm9 C7 Gm7 3 C7 Gm9 C7 B♭6
I want a girl, a warm heart-ed girl, with eyes like the deep blue
F Gm9 C7 Gm9 3 C7
sea, Hair made of gold, and lips that are bold Who'll
Gm9 C7 F6 F7 B♭6 B°
al-ways be true to me. And when my search-ing was through, And my
F6 B° F6 F7 B♭6 B°
dream still had-n't come true, I start-ed home-ward to find, Love was

F6 B° F6 Gm9 C7
wait - ing here all the time! I found a girl a
Gm9 C7 Gm9 C7 B♭6 F
warm heart - ed girl, with eyes like the deep blue sea
Gm9 C7 Gm9 C7 Gm9 C7 A7+
Hair made of gold, and lips that are bold, Who'll al - ways be true to
Dm7 B♭7 E♭maj7 Dm6
me.

Brazil

Lyric by
S. K. RUSSELL

Brazilian Samba by
ARO BARROSO

SUGGESTED REGISTRATIONS

Single-Manual Organs
8' I II

Vibrato: On

Play: Upper & Lower

General Electronic & Pipe Organs
Upper: Clarinet 8' (or 16')
Trumpet 8'
Lower: Flute 8' (or Melodia 8')
Diapason 8' Bassoon 8'
(or Viola 8')
Pedal: 8'
Vibrato: On

Drawbar Organs
Upper: 00 8373 441

Lower: (00) 6443 423 (0)

Pedal: 4 - (2)
Vibrato: On

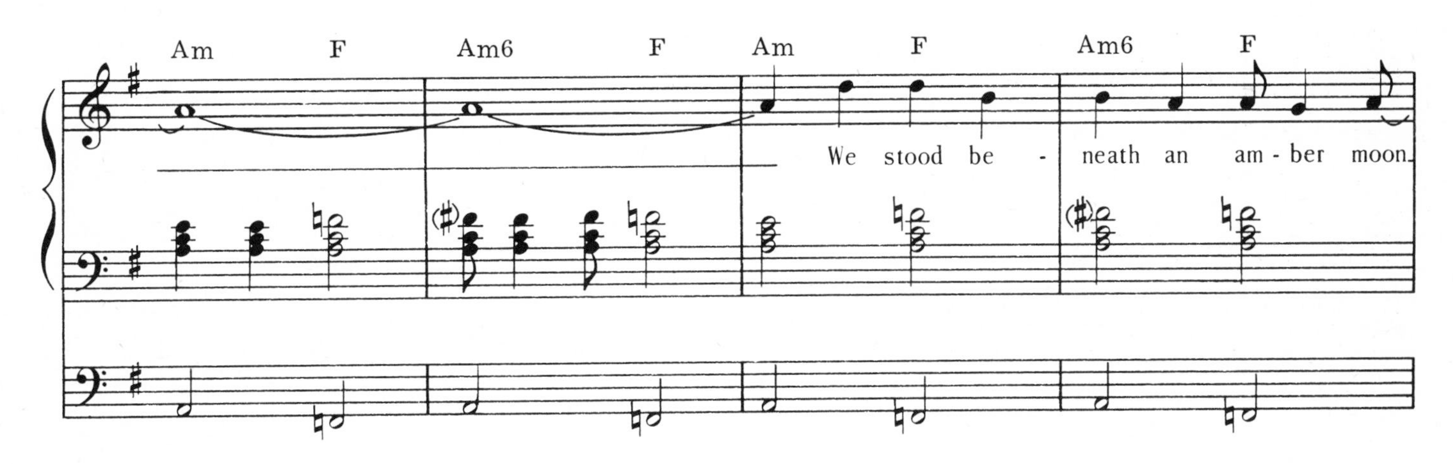

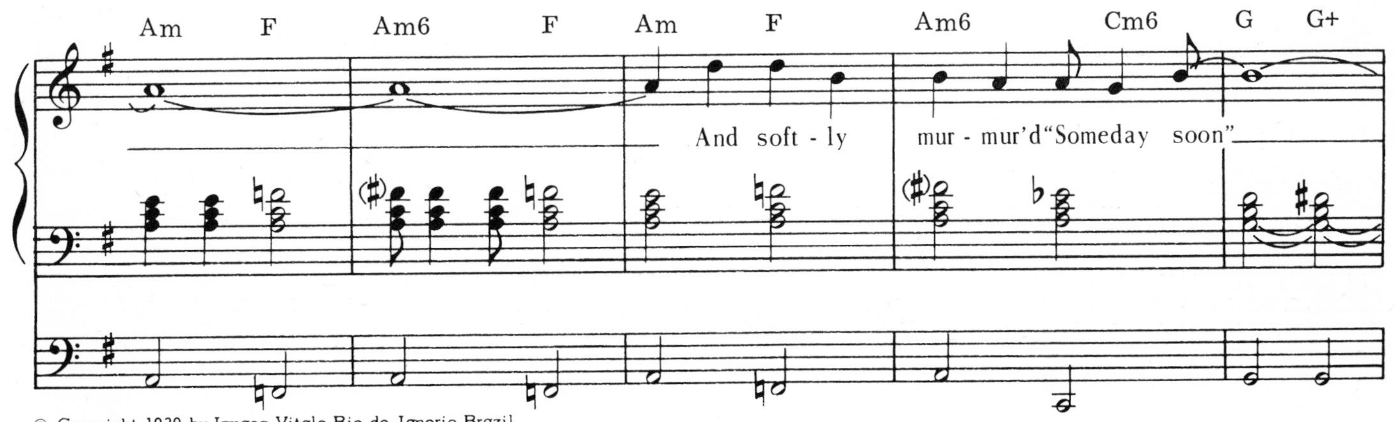

G6 Gmaj7 (5#) Am Fmaj7 Am6 F#o G G7 Gb7 F7 E7
We kissed and cling to - ge - ther, Then
Dm E7 Dm E7
to - mor-row was an - oth-er day The morn-ing
Dm E7
found me miles a - way with still a mil - lion things to say
Am F Am6 F Am F
Now

Am
Cm
F#o
G
D7
— When twi - light dims the sky a - bove, — Re - call - ing
G
C#o
Am7
E9b
D7
thrills of our love, — There's one thing I'm cer-tain of; —
G G+ G6 Gmaj7(5#) Am Fmaj7 Am6 F#o G C+ G6 Gmaj7(5#)
— Re - turn — I will — to
Am Fmaj7 Am6 F#o G G+ G6 G+ G G+ G6
old — Bra - zil. —

Tell Me Marianne

(A MEDIA LUZ)

English Adaptation by
BOB MUSEL

Music by
EDGARDO DONATO

SUGGESTED REGISTRATIONS

Single-Manual Organs		General Electronic & Pipe Organs		Drawbar Organs	
8' 4' I II		Upper:	Trumpet 8' Strings 8'	Upper:	43 6804 434
Vibrato:	On	Lower:	Flute 8' 4' Diapason 8'	Lower:	(00) 7554 512(0)
Play:	Upper & Lower	Pedal:	8'	Pedal:	4 - (2)
		Vibrato:	On	Vibrato:	On

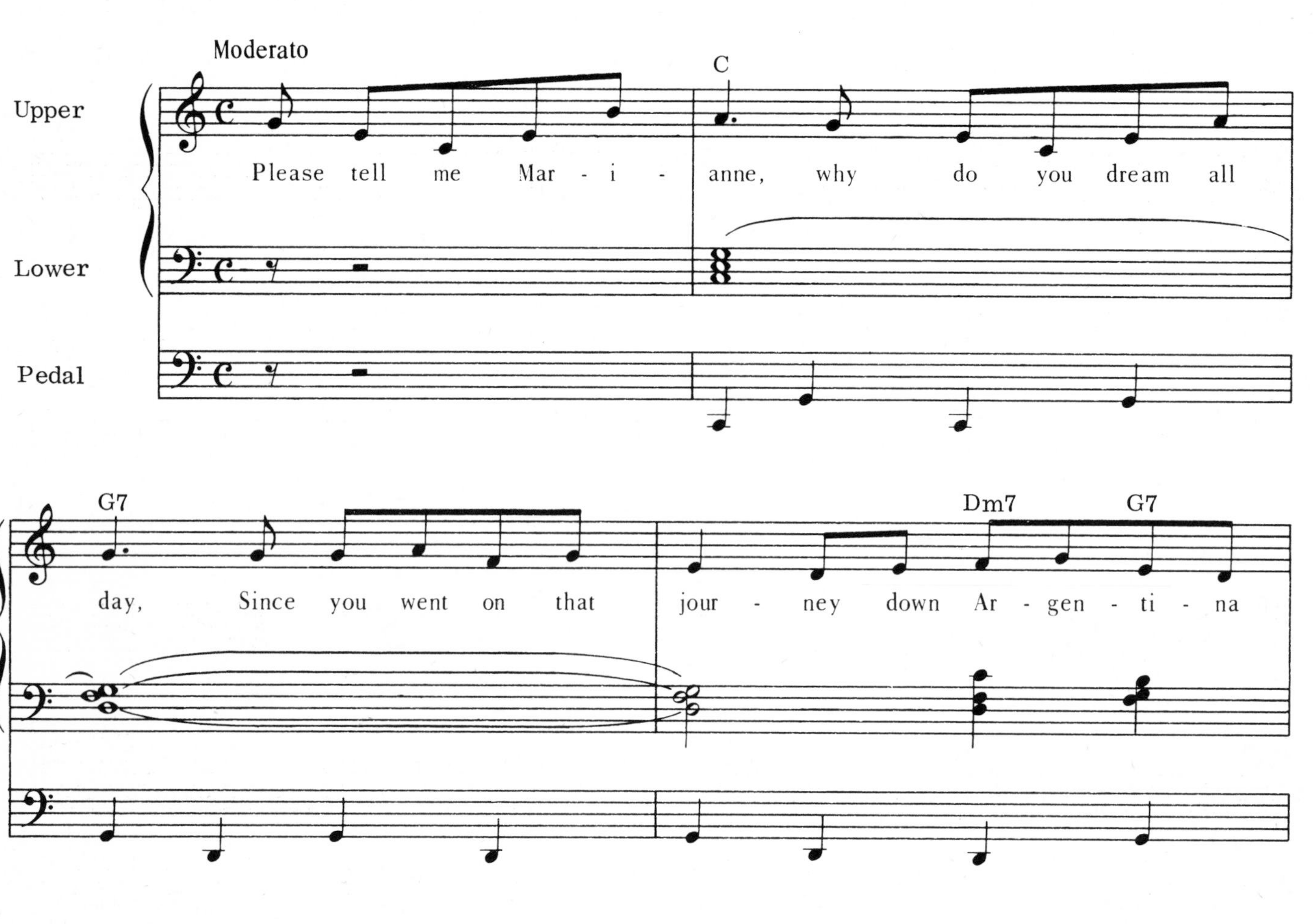

G7
tune That made your heart go
Dm7 G7
danc - ing be - neath the Pam - pas
C Cm
moon? Was it
Cm
Pan - cho or was it
G7
Pe - dro Was it
Pab - lo who trem-bled at your
Cm
touch,
Fm
Was it some hand - some
Gauch - o
G7
vow- ing he loved you too
Cm
much? Was it

G7
some - one you met in
Ri - o in the
dawn - ing when car - ni - val was
Cm
gay,
Fm
Who made your dark eyes
glist - en?
G7
List - en, your thoughts are far a -
C
way. You smile so wist-ful - ly as on - ly lov - ers
G7
can, Down there in Ar - gen - ti - na what hap-pened Ma - ri - anne?
Dm7
G7
C

A Garden In Granada

Words & Music by
SAM M. LEWIS,
ABEL BAER
& ION VASILESCU

SUGGESTED REGISTRATIONS

Single-Manual Organs
8' I V
Vibrato: On
Play: Upper & Lower

General Electronic & Pipe Organs
Upper: Strings 8'
Lower: Flute 8' 4' (or Melodia 8')
Pedal: 8'
Vibrato: On

Drawbar Organs
Upper: 00 8888 666
Lower: (00) 6628 224 (0)
Pedal: 5 - (2)
Vibrato: On

tacet
C C+ C6 C+
C+
My heart was lone - ly and ne - glect - ed; Who knew that heav - en was so
Dm Bb D6 Bb Dm tacet
G7 G#o Dm7 Dm75b
near; Your kiss - es were so un - ex - pect - ed; Who
G7 Dm7 G+ C F C Dm6 B7
knew that life could be so dear. Gone are the
E7 E+ E7 Am
flow - ers, And ev - 'ry lit - tle blade of grass,

E7 Am7 D7 Am7 D7
But we'll keep those hours, And what ev - er
Fm6 G7 Dm7 tacet C C+ C6 C+
comes to pass We'll see A Gar - den in Gra - na - da;
C C+ Dm B♭ D6 B♭ Dm tacet
We'll see a star - ry spang- led sky; There'll be A Gar - den in Gra-
G7 G#o Dm7 Dm7♭5 G7 Dm7 G9 C Dm B C
- na - da As long as there's a you and I

Non Dimenticar

(DON'T FORGET)

English Lyric by
SHELLEY DOBBINS

Music by
P. G. REDI

SUGGESTED REGISTRATIONS

Single-Manual Organs
8' II III IV
Vibrato: On
Play: Upper & Lower

General Electronic & Pipe Organs
Upper: Flute 8' Strings 4' (or 8')
Lower: Melodia 8' (or Diapason 8')
Pedal: 16'
Vibrato: On

Drawbar Organs
Upper: 00 8765 000
Lower: (00) 4511 111 (0)
Pedal: 4 - (3)
Vibrato: No. V3

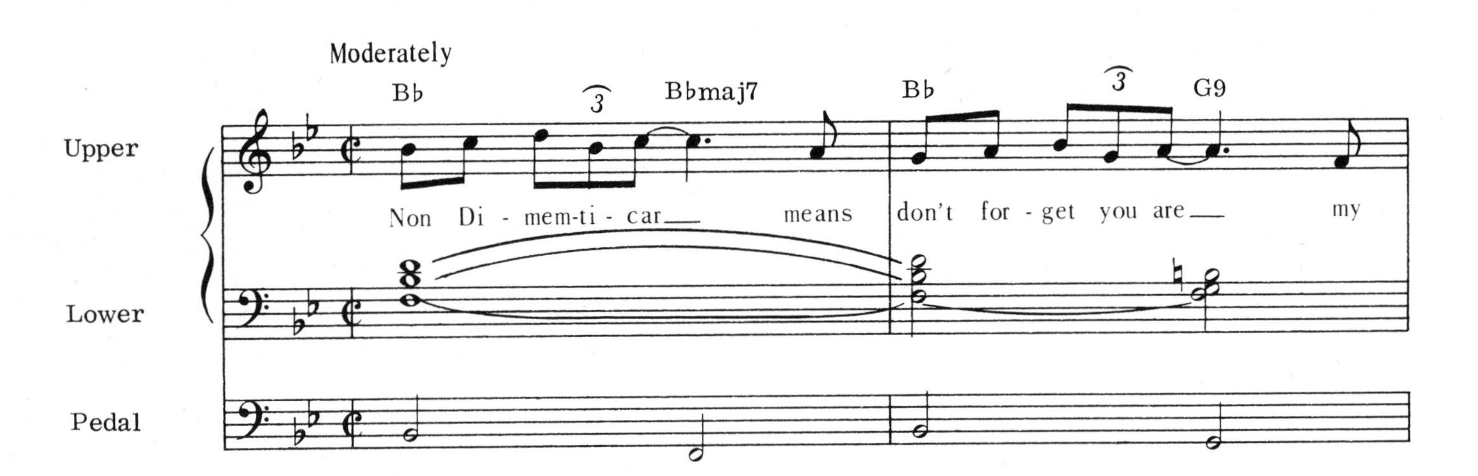

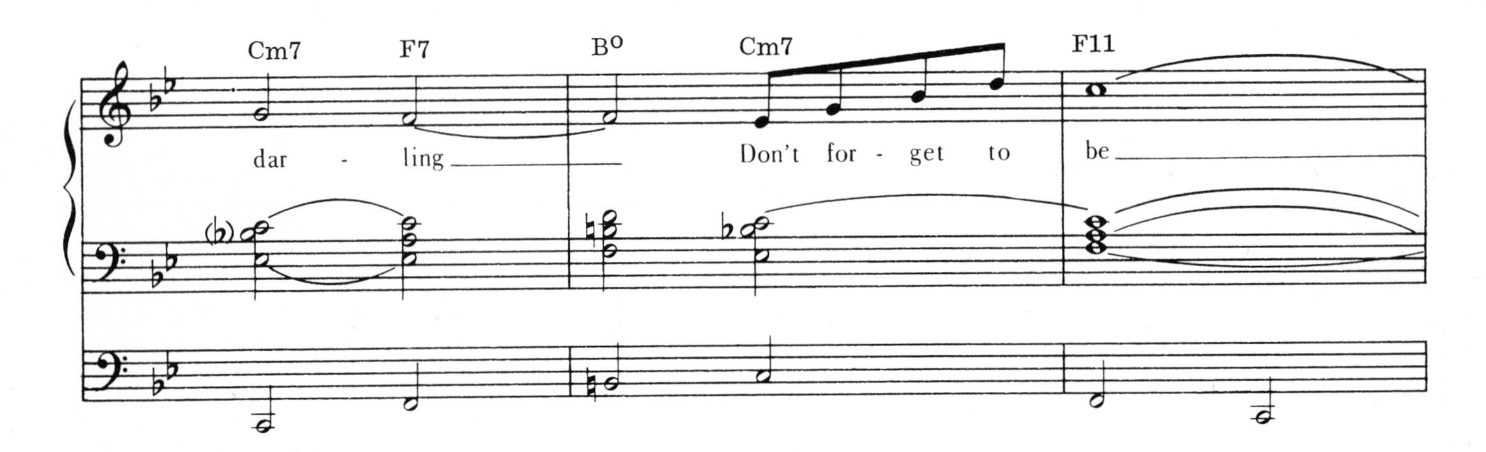

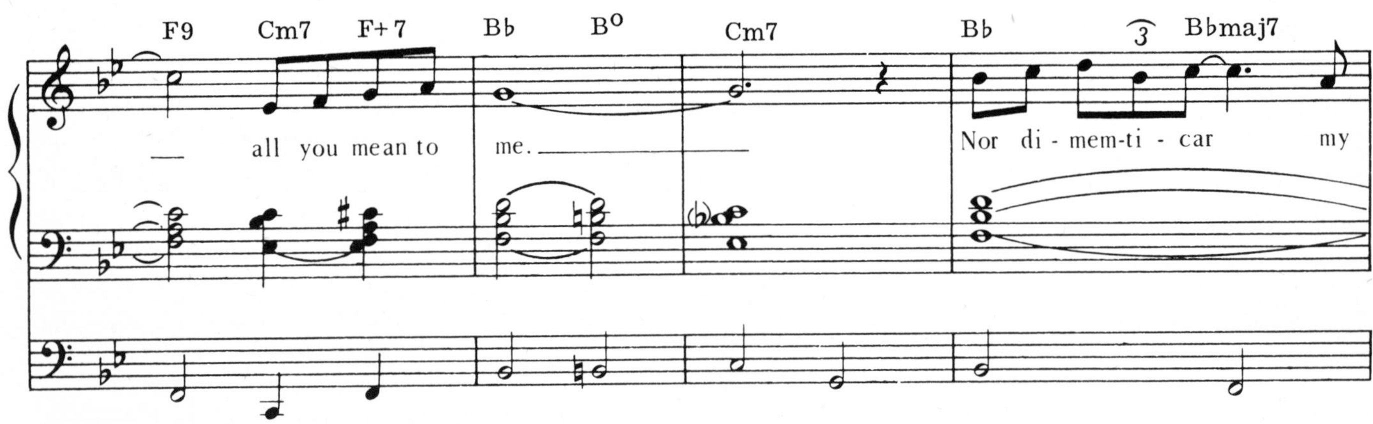

Bb G9 Cm7 F7 Bo Cm7
love is like a star, my dar - ling Shin - ing bright and
F11 F9 Cm7 F7 Bb Ebm6
clear just be - cause you're here.
Bbo Bb7 Fm7 Bb7 Fm7 Bb7 Bb7+
Please do not for - get that our lips have met and I've held you
Eb Ebmaj7 Eb6 Gm7 C7
tight dear, Was it dreams a - go my heart felt this

Printed in Great Britain by
The Thetford Press Limited, Thetford, Norfolk